1 | The Illustrated Encyclopedia of the Animal Kingdom

The Illustrated Encyclopedia of the Animal Kingdom

The Danbury Press

Editorial: HERBERT KONDO—Editor

JENNY E. TESAR—Senior Editor

LYNN T. KAGAN—Assistant Editor

CONSTANCE HINTZ—Editorial Assistant

KATHLEEN LEERBURGER—Indexer

Art and Design: JACK JAGET

Production Supervision: THE STONEHOUSE PRESS

Editorial, original English edition: PERCY KNAUTH, DALE MCADOO, GEORG ZAPPLER

Zoological Consultant: RICHARD G. VAN GELDER, Chairman & Curator,
Department of Mammalogy, The American Museum of Natural
History, New York, New York

The Danbury Press, a division of Grolier Enterprises, Inc.

Publisher–ROBERT B. CLARKE.

Marketing Director–ROBERT G. BARTNER.

Creative Director–GILBERT EVANS.

Publishing Consultant–DAVID MENDELSOHN.

Assistant to the Publisher—VALERIE HARBOUR.

ISBN 0-7172-8100-0
Library of Congress Catalog Card Number 71-141898
© 1970, 1971 Fratelli Fabbri Editori, Milan
Text: © 1972 Grolier Enterprises, Inc.
Illustrations*: © 1968, 1971, 1972, Fratelli Fabbri Editori, Milan
The Illustrated Encyclopedia of the Animal Kingdom was originally
translated and adapted from *Gli animali e il loro mondo*,
originally published in Italy under the direction of Professor
Antonio Valle, Director of the Museum of Natural Science, Bergamo.

*With the exception of the following illustrations: Zigmund Leszczynski-
104, 105; M. Wiedman-cover, 2, 3, 5, 45, 47, 86, 121, 137.

Printed in the United States of America

PHOTO CREDITS

Atlas-Vienna-Bavaria—130; Australian News & Information Bureau-Canberra—68, 93; Barnaby's Picture
Library-Nash—13, R. W. Kennedy—14, S. Kalman—60, 88; A. E. Brehn-Turin—102; Bruce Coleman LTD-J.
Van Wormer—25, 43, 130; R. Die—111; E. Dulevant-Turin—93, 144; E. P. S.—104, 105, 143; Lucio Gaggero
—32, 62, 67, 85, 98; G. S. Giacomelli-S. Chiara-Naples—115, 141; Como Guissani—117; Igmar Holmasen-
Malmkoping—40; Institute of Geology and Paleontology—83; Institute for Scientific Research, Luiro—82,
93; Royal Institute of Natural Sciences-Brussels—123; Jesse—44, 58; Frank Lane-H. H. Schroeder—83;
Christian Lederer-Bavaria—69; Liedmann-Bavaria—106, 122; Longo—69;
R. Maltini—22, 140; Marconato—16, 17; A. Margicco—11, 16, 18, 19, 24, 30, 34, 35, 45, 51, 53, 57, 63, 65, 69,
72, 76, 89, 99, 103, 112, 115, 117, 132, 133, 137, 138, 139; G. Mazza—14, 15, 28, 29, 31, 65, 83, 110, 112, 115, 143;
Monaco Aquarium—80; Marineland Aquarium-Palos Verdes—110; Manfred Melde—101; Museum of
Natural History-Milan—112; Hauff Museum-Holzmaden-Wurttemberg—70; N. H. P. A.-Betsoms-Anthony
Bannister—14, 15; J. Blossom—14, 105; Lionel E. Day—73; Natural History Photo Agency-S. Dalton—
59, 129; Oischki, Florence—30; Carl E. Ostmam-Bromma—69; Pasotti—26; Dr. Lino Pellegrini—18, 19,
71, 110, 143; CCM General Biological Inc.—16, 17; Willis Petersox—46, 91, 131; Picturepoint—94, 95;
Paul Popper-London—69, 73, 79, 95, 97, 108, 127; A. Pozzi—16, 17, 25, 33, 35, 84, 93, 103, 117; Relini—
141; Photo Researchers-Hillingdon—11, Des Bartlett—26, 47, 109, 119, 131, 135, J. Burton—37, 67, 116,
118, 139; Rod Allin—50, J. Dermid—73, Peter Jackson—108, Russ Kinne—41, N. Myers—136, Simon—
72; Roebild, Muller—12, 13, 39, 41, 87, 125; Roloc, Washington—100, 134; A. P. Rossi—69, 76, 81, 84, 87,
126, 129; G. Rossi-Institute of Botanical Science, University of Milan—20, 21; Miami Seaquarium—48, 81,
139; S. E. F., Turin—18, 19, 81, 123, 126, 127; Sirman, Dimt—78, 86, 114, 134; Misa Susini—89; Anton
Thau-Bavaria—10, 38, 123, 124; American Museum of Natural History—35; British Museum of Natural
History—66; Turbilder Okapia—18, 19, 36, 37, 50, 55, 56, 61, 73, 78, 84, 89, 101, 104, 125, 137; Tomisch
—56; V-Dia-Verlag-Heideberg—43; G. Vecchia—48, 107; Peter Ward—90; D. P. Wilson—18, 19, 31, 70, 108,
141, 142, ZFA Dusseldorf—25, 42, 88, 90; Frankfurt Zoo—9, 72, 92, 103; Roma Zoo—20, 21;

Contents

Foreword

*M*ost people find the animal world fascinating, and the intricate and graceful shapes of shells, the bright colors and airy grace of butterflies, and the songs and beauty of birds have their dedicated admirers and hobbyists. Until now, such interest has been largely of entertainment value, and our zoos, aquariums, and natural history museums report ever-increasing numbers of visitors who are intrigued with the form, the function, and the behavior of the myriad animals that share this planet with man. But now that man's burgeoning population is threatening this animal life, and with it the very existence of man, these same creatures may be the source of solutions to our problems.

Many of our rivers and lakes, once clear and teeming with life, are now chemical cesspools intolerant of life. Our once fertile fields are now sterile, sustained only by artificial fertilizers, and are used for crops that survive only by the dubious protection of more chemicals—herbicides and insecticides. All these poisons find their way into our soil, into our water, and eventually into the seas, where they pollute the entire planet.

For every species that is endangered by chemical poisons, there is another that is threatened directly by man, often for the most transient of reasons. The great blue whale, the largest animal that ever lived on earth, now seems doomed to extinction as a provider of dog food, fertilizer, and a small amount of margarine. The lithe and graceful leopard, too, may pass from the face of the earth to provide coats to satisfy the vanity of affluent women. And the noble polar bear, the aristocrat of the North, is diminishing before the guns of hunters, to provide nothing more than a visible symbol of a man's self-questioning of his own virility.

With a world population that is doubling every thirty-five years, man is drawing faster and faster on the limited resources of the earth. He does not seem to realize that the destruction of the environment and the upset of ecological balances threaten not only the existence of other creatures, but also of man himself. A third of the world is already at the starvation level, and famine and pestilence once more present the specters of death for all mankind.

Ecological problems are not new, for they have existed since the beginning of life on earth. Every one of the animals displayed so beautifully on the pages of these volumes has faced and solved the same problems that now face man. Instead of being bent on the alteration and destruction of the environment, man must learn how to come into harmony with it. Man must utilize the same checks and balances that govern animal populations to come into equilibrium with the environment.

There is much to be learned from these animals, for most of the great technological discoveries of man are but crude duplicates of the refined systems of some other creatures. Bats and dolphins have echo-location systems far more sophisticated than man's sonar. Fireflies produce light virtually without heat. Whales can dive to great depths and return quickly to the surface without gaseous damage to their brains. Bees can see ultraviolet light, and rattlesnakes are sensitive detectors of infrared radiation. Kangaroo rats live their entire lives without drinking water, manufacturing what they need from the metabolic breakdown of their food. These are but a few of the mechanisms that animals have evolved and refined and which man has tried to imitate.

In these volumes, then, is more than entertainment. These are sourcebooks of natural experimentation that have stood the test of time, millions of years of evolution. Each of the structures that makes every species unique is an evolutionary refinement with a function, whether it be the hydraulic pressure system that starfish use for locomotion or the hairy baskets into which bees pack pollen. There is much, too, to be learned from the social organization of animals, whether it be the noisy, but unviolent clans of howler monkeys or the tyrannical monarchies of macaque troops. Each has its purpose and function within the limitations of the environment.

Here in these books is source material for the future of man. He is a relative newcomer on the evolutionary scene, and he has attempted to dominate and to destroy the environment. It is now clear that his concept of altering nature is leading only to disaster. The evolutionary message is clear: he must either change his methods or face extinction from his own folly. There are many examples in these books of how he might adapt to his environment, rather than attempt to adapt the environment to him. Instead of "man against nature" he must choose to be "man with nature," and to come into harmony and equilibrium with the natural world around him.

RICHARD G. VAN GELDER

Chairman and Curator, Department of Mammalogy
The American Museum of Natural History, New York, New York
September, 1970

*A*s humans, we pride ouselves on our great and intricate inventions, our works of art, our buildings and cities, and our ever expanding domination of the planet.

The animal kingdom can boast of at least as long a catalogue of inventions, as breathtaking an array of form and color, and certainly a much longer period of successful occupancy of the environment. Animals have been an integral part of the planet earth for several billion years. In the course of this time they have undergone innumerable transformations. Today's animal species range from microscopic organisms to 130-ton whales, and can be numbered in the hundreds of thousands. If extinct species are also counted, the totals become astronomical.

Animals live in the water, on land, and in the air. They can be found in almost any type of environment: from the polar ice caps to the equator, from mountain tops to ocean deeps. Animals have achieved environment success not with tools and machinery, but through the gradual evolution of their bodies and internal make-up. When swimming, fish use torpedo-shaped flexible bodies, powered with energy produced by burning food. Moles have shovel-shaped hands with which to dig. Birds solve aerodynamic problems by way of wing and feather. Heat regulation in mammals is accomplished through the possession of layers of fat and fur. On the more sensational side, bats use an ultrasonic echo-location system. Some fish produce electric fields with which to find their way. Bees perform dances when telling their hivemates about the distance and direction of a food source. And birds navigate by using the sun and the stars as a compass.

The fantastic diversity of animal life could never be discussed properly unless arranged in some kind of a system. Zoologists have worked out large and small groupings among animals. These categories are based on similarities and differences in structure, development, and behavior. To the layman, some of these categories make sense; others take a lot of explaining. For example, that flies and gnats should be grouped together seems fairly obvious, but that barnacles and lobsters are closely related may come as a surprise.

This encyclopedia covers in comprehensive detail, all the major groups of animals, their membership, their appearance and ancestry, their geographic distribution, their living habits and relationships to the world at large.

Animals with Backbones

Human beings, sponges, lions, worms, robins, lizards, bumblebees, and crabs: what do they have in common? They are all animals. There are some one million kinds, or species, of animals living today. They range from one-celled amoebas to giant whales.

Some of these animals have backbones. We call them vertebrates. Animals without backbones are called invertebrates.

Running along the back of a vertebrate is a column of jointed bony segments called vertebrae. If you move your hand up and down along the middle of your back, you can feel your backbone. If you move your hand along the back of a cat or a dog or a lizard, you can feel its backbone. This structure lends a great deal of flexible support to the body. Attached to the vertebrae are other bones of the skeleton and many kinds of muscles. These are needed to flex and bend, to run and jump, to fly or to swim.

Many of the animals that are most familiar to us are vertebrates: fish, frogs, snakes, turtles, birds, cows, horses—and man. This volume provides a general overview of the vertebrates, man's closest relatives in the animal kingdom. You will see that there are certain basic requirements for successful living. Food has to be obtained, enemies avoided, and the next generation provided for. The cycle is always the same—from birth to parenthood to death. In the process, new life is born. And, although the problems faced by all animals are the same, they are solved by different body shapes and living habits.

The lively song bird and squirrel shown below are typical vertebrates. They are alert, active animals.

No great zoological know-how is needed to pick out the vertebrates from the rest of the animals that buzz, crawl, and scurry around us. The fleshy skin-covered body with its internal skeleton and its generally graceful movements is almost always immediately recognizable. A silvery trout in the brook, a splashing frog, an elegant bird in flight, a purring cat, a dog straining on its leash— all these are obviously closer relations of man than the jellyfish, butterfly, or snail.

Long before there was anything alive on the barren rocks of continental masses, a multitude of living things existed in the oceans. Microscopic one-celled animals, sponges, jellyfish, worms, and jointed-legged animals with soft bodies encased in crab-like armor flourished in the waters of the world. These animals existed for tens of millions of years before a small torpedo-shaped organism with an internal stiffening

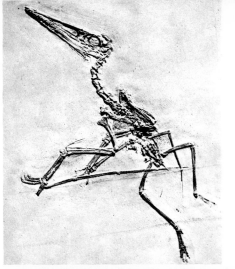

This is the skeleton of an extinct reptile called a pterodactyl. Its name means "wing foot." The long finger bone supported a layer of skin that stretched to the back legs. The pterodactyl was a glider.

By hunching up, this tree frog (middle) can conserve moisture during the day. Later, at night, this amphibian will be quite active catching insects.

The yawning hippo (bottom) is not as lazy as it seems. It spent the whole night walking and feeding on land. Now it is resting in the plant-covered water.

rod running the length of its body was born to become the forefather of fishes, amphibians, reptiles, birds, and mammals.

Later in vertebrate history, the stiffening rod became surrounded by bony rings, or vertebrae. The evolution of this rod can be compared to a great invention such as that of the wheel. Once it was there, innumerable variations and refinements became possible. It took a fish for there to be an amphibian, and an amphibian before a reptile could be born. Birds and mammals both evolved from reptiles to become what they are today. To return to the wheel analogy: somebody had to invent a wagon before the racing car could be developed.

Look about and observe the success of the vertebrates. Despite the many ecological problems caused by mankind, vertebrates can still be found in every type of habitat on earth. Fish still inhabit oceans by the millions; the croaking of frogs remains a common summer sound. The heyday of the reptiles passed with the last of the dinosaurs; but reptiles such as turtles, lizards, snakes, and crocodiles have managed to survive. Birds can be seen everywhere and exist by the thousands of species. Many mammals

Snakes can be considered the most successful group of living reptiles. Many snakes kill their prey with poison. The deadly African green mamba (below) lives south of the Sahara.

The ostrich (left) is a bird, but it cannot fly. It lives in the open grasslands of Africa, where it sometimes runs as fast as 40 miles an hour.

Mammals are among the most recent vertebrates to evolve. Some, like the African elephant (below, left), are known for their large size and bulk. Others, like the beaver adding to its dam (below, right), are known for their ability to change the environment that surrounds them.

Some birds (top) are very aggressive. This individual is scolding an intruder. His sharp beak helps to make his threat all the more frightening.

The meek, clown-faced fish (below) protects itself by changing into a bristling balloon. The stiff pines that are now very small, pop out all over when the fish fills its body with air.

The lizard (opposite) looks like a dangerous dragon in this picture. Actually, it is an iguana, a harmless vegetarian.

have become extinct. We have favored some, such as dogs and cats, and they have thrived. We also raise plant-eaters such as cows and sheep to provide meat. The smaller rodents, mice and rats, have done well alongside man, and until recently forests and grasslands teemed with large and medium-sized mammals. Bison, zebras, deer, and elephants browsed and grazed. They in turn provided food for the lions, tigers, and wolves.

In general, then, the vertebrates, although they are but one of some twenty-five major groups, or phyla, which together constitute the animal kingdom, are a dominant group indeed. They are an important part of any environment. And, of course, included among them is man, *Homo sapiens*.

Animals survive by adapting to their environment. The streamlined, scaled body of the trout (top left) is well designed for cutting through water. The snout of the wild boar (top right) is ideal for rooting. This animal can eat food that others are not able to find. The lion (right) has great muscular coordination which helps him capture speedy prey.

Shapes and Proportions

Other than sharing the commonly held characteristics that mark all vertebrates, the animals of this group are not much alike. There is a fantastic diversity of form. Although each has a head, a trunk, a tail, and two pairs of limbs, the variations played upon this basic theme are almost limitless.

Heads, for instance, all have organs for eating as well as for seeing, hearing, and thinking. But they come in a multitude of shapes and sizes. Some tiny animals have disproportionately large heads, while there are big, pinheaded animals that also do very well in their particular spot in nature. Some have squat snouts that barely protrude from the cheeks, while others boast long trunks. The head may be attached to the body by a long sinuous neck or by a scarcely perceptible joining to the back.

The body, which houses the all-important digestive and reproductive systems, is sometimes lean and sometimes fat. It may be capable of great flexibility or held rigidly.

Legs, the main means of transportation, can be massive columns, stilts, or paddle-like flippers. The feet at the end of those legs are sometimes clawed and sometimes hoofed. Some vertebrates are flat-footed with five toes and the heel bearing the impact of the earth; others stand on the tip of one large toe, with the heel raised high off the ground.

At first glance lizards, mice, and dogs may appear to have nothing in common. A closer look, though, reveals that they do. Besides having backbones, they have long tails, clawed toes, and fast-acting muscles for speedy movement.

17

The strange looking animal on the right is a bat. Bats are the only mammals that have completely mastered flying.

Both animals below are fish. Yet their appearances are very different.

A tail, if it is on a horse, is mostly a fly swatter. On a male peacock, it is a great fan carried upward to attract the female's attention. The pig's corkscrew tail appears to function only as an entertainment for the rest of the world.

The external covering may be scaled, as in fish and reptiles. This allows for flexibility while protecting the soft flesh. In birds the external covering consists of feathers, which provide light-weight insulation. Mammals have a covering of fur or hair.

Extra attachments are frequently added to the top layer, like the horns of goats, the spines of porcupines, the antlers of deer, the combs of chickens, and the crests of lizards.

Some animals look very peculiar to us. However, in every kind of animal there is a definite adaptive purpose to its general shape and all its particular parts. The turtle, for

The indri (top) is a lemur, but looks more like an ape. Indris prefer to stay in tree branches. When they do walk on land, they stand on their back legs and hold their short arms above their heads.

The sea horse (left) is a fish. Other fish swim with their tails behind them; the sea horse swims vertically.

Salamanders (far left) are amphibians. Some salamanders live on land; others live in the water. All, however, breed in water.

Most vertebrates have tails. The rabbit's is so small it can barely be seen.

Some birds have extraordinary tails. The lyre bird (above right) and the pheasant (right) use their beautiful tails to attract mates.

The snout of the anteater (left) is well shaped for getting ants. The shoe-bill (right) uses its beak to dig fish and frogs from the bottom of rivers.

example, clumping slowly along in its shell, has survived for millions of years. The long-necked ostrich is flightless, but can run faster than most other birds can fly. The elephant's trunk is just as efficient a feeding and smelling mechanism as the dog's more conventional muzzle. No animal is ill-equipped for the life it leads. In fact, each has the necessary paraphernalia to render it perfect for its own special way of life.

We might, for instance, think of a lion as the ideally equipped mammal. Its large head, held nobly on a well-proportioned neck, houses an alert brain and a powerful set of jaws equipped with frighteningly effi-cient teeth. Its body, rippling with muscles, and its long, powerful legs assure this ani-mal of the ability to catch its prey.

But the little house mouse is even more successful than the lion. Lions are primarily found on the plains of Africa. But house mice can be found in almost every habitat used by man. They even manage to outwit man and share his house and board. Also, there are much larger populations of mice than of lions. Mice owe their success to in-conspicuous size, great numbers of offspring, an effective set of chiselling and grinding teeth, and the ability to share in man's agri-cultural success.

The Realm of Water

The planet earth should really have been called the planet water, since more of its surface is taken up by this substance than by soil. Most animal groups started in the water, and so did the vertebrates, in the form of primitive fish some 500 million years ago. Vertebrates still dominate the aquatic habitats of the world, dwelling near the surface and on the bottom of rivers, estuaries, lakes, oceans and inland seas.

Vertebrates owe their elongated, internally supported and muscularly flexible bodies to their beginning struggles in water. Only those vertebrates able to survive in this environment reproduced and passed on their physical characteristics to future generations. Later, some vertebrates crawled onto land and were able to survive. But the ancestral seas have attracted many descendants of land-adapted stocks. Well-known examples are seals and porpoises (mammals), penguins (birds), and sea turtles and extinct ichthyosaurs (reptiles). These secondarily aquatic forms have fins or flippers instead of legs; some of them have evolved a fish-shaped form.

The shark (left) is as dangerous as it is beautiful. Its torpedo shape, broad fins and whipping tail make it one of the strongest vertebrates in the sea.

The sea lion (below) is also a vertebrate that lives in water. It swims so well that it can outswim many fish.

Living On Land

Inhabitants of the grass-lands of Africa, the zebras' legs are adapted for hard running. Their high-crowned teeth resist the wear of chewing tough grasses.

For about 100 million years the vertebrates were strictly water creatures. Then, in the first amphibians, fins evolved into weight-bearing legs. Today's salamanders, frogs, and toads are direct descendants of these early land dwellers. Additional "land inventions" evolved among the reptiles: dry skin and the protectively-shelled egg.

A final physiological advance, the ability to maintain a steady internal body heat despite fluctuations in outside temperatures, evolved in mammals and birds. Over the course of millions of years of evolution, only insects have equalled vertebrates in the successful exploitation of terrestrial habitats.

At one time giant lizard-like dinosaurs lived on the earth. Today, most reptiles, like the skink (upper left) are small animals.

Amphibians can live in water or on land. The toad (above) is an amphibian. It may live on land but it must return to water to reproduce.

The roadrunner (left) can move as quickly on land as many four-legged creatures. Most birds must fly when they need to move fast.

Into the Air

The air can be thought of as the third major environmental layer. It envelops both water and land. Vertebrates moved onto land before flying species evolved. The most successful aerialists are, of course, the birds. They developed from land-dwelling reptiles some 140 million years ago and now number about 8,500 species. Another reptilian lineage, the pterosaurs, also managed to rise aloft. But they were not as well adapted as their feathered cousins. The bats, a specialized mam-

malian group, are nighttime flyers (birds are mostly day creatures).

The aerial habitat is always a temporary abode. It is used for fast travel, to escape from enemies, and to hunt for food. Ultimately the pull of gravity reclaims even the most enduring of fliers. Hence, nesting, and other activities require a return to more solid surroundings.

Flocks of birds, like the snow geese (far left), are a common sight during times of migration. Some birds travel thousands of miles.

The hummingbird (left) can hover "motionless" in the air as he eats. The shape of his body makes this possible.

The bat (below) flys, but not on feathered wings. It flaps through the air on membranes of skin that are stretched over the bones of its limbs.

27

Patents for Living

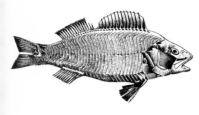

Among the vertebrates, a trout is obviously different from an eagle. One is a fish, the other a bird. Also, a trout can quite readily be distinguished from a guppy. Yet both are clearly more similar to one another than either is to any bird.

Zoologists have taken these basic differences and used them to divide the major category, or phylum, of vertebrates into subgroups called classes. Thus bony fish constitute one class of vertebrates and birds another. In addition, the amphibians, the reptiles, and the mammals each are in separate classes. Each class has its own "zone of adaptation." A basic set of physical characteristics has evolved in each class. It is these characteristics that enable the animals to survive in their adaptive zones.

Fishes and Water

A fish out of water is truly out of its element. Everything about a fish is keyed to its particular adaptive zone. The streamlined body, the mucus-coated scaly skin, the whipping tail, the ruddering and balancing fins, all facilitate movement through water.

Beneath the sleek covering of a fish lie rows of muscles (above). These provide the wave-like curves that propel the fish through water.

The sturgeon (below) stirs up mud with its flattened nose. It feeds on the organisms it uproots.

Like all vertebrates, fish are bilaterally symmetrical. That is, the two sides of the body are mirror images of one another. Their body plan is the same as in all backboned animals. Essentially, it is a pierced cylinder with a food canal running inside from front to back and open at both ends. Above the food canal is the spinal column, a series of

interlocking discs called vertebrae that lend internal support to the body. Above the vertebral column, and enclosed by outgrowths from each disc, lies the central nerve cord. The brain is a ballooning out of the nerve cord at the front end. It is protected by a bony capsule, the cranium.

The body cylinder is made up of similar segments of muscle fibers repeated from end to end and placed on either side of the spinal column. The muscle fibers in each segment run from front to back, so that when they contract they bend the body. The propulsive forces that move a fish through water are produced by the serial contraction of these muscles. During swimming, the contraction of each segment takes place after that of the segment in front of it. In this way, waves of

A fish (above) swims through water by curving its body from side to side.

Freshwater trout (above left) are a favorite source of food and sport for many people.

The male guppy's beautiful colors (left) are the product of long selective breeding. Guppies are often kept in aquariums as pets.

29

Some fish swim alone; others stay in groups. The picture on the right is an example of a group, or "school," of fish.

Fish live in many temperatures. Some live in cold or temperate water. Others, like the one below, stay in warm tropical seas.

curvature are passed down the body, alternately on each side. The large tail fin exerts a powerful propellerlike thrust as the waves of contractions pass through it.

Most fishes have two sets of paired fins, the pectorals, just behind the head, and the pelvics, usually located farther back. Unpaired fins located along the midline on top and below are also present. Usually there is a dorsal fin above and an anal fin behind the vent. In general, the fins are stabilizers and balancers; the pectoral fins are also used for turning.

The front end of the food tube is the mouth. This is usually surrounded by hinged jaws that swing apart to take in food. Feeding ranges from scraping algae to eating other fish.

In a fish, breathing involves extracting oxygen from water at the same time that accumulated carbon dioxide is discharged from the bloodstream. This gas exchange takes place in the skin that lines the gills. This skin is porous and has many blood vessels. Many primitive fishes also had lungs for taking in gulps of air. Some lung-breathing fishes still exist. In most modern fishes, however, lungs have evolved into an air bladder. This functions as an internal adjustable "balloon" for regulating buoyancy.

Blood circulation in fishes is a relatively simple cycle. A two-chambered heart acts as a pump. Aerated blood flows from the gills to the organs and tissues where the oxygen is extracted. Deoxygenated blood then flows back to the heart, which contracts and pumps it into the gills for more oxygen.

Fish have no physiological means of raising or cooling their body temperature. They are dependent solely on the temperature of the water in which they live. But fish seek out "preferred" environments by swimming into warmer or colder currents.

Depending on whether a fish lives in fresh water or salt water, it has different problems of excretion. In fresh water, the kidneys must constantly pump out excess water to prevent the normally salty blood from be-

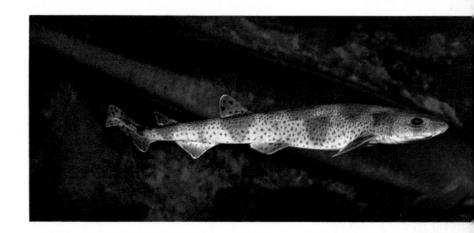

The fish on the left is a pike. Its body has a bony skeleton. The two fish below are sharks; they have skeletons that are mostly cartilage.

coming too dilute. In the ocean, the problem is just the opposite; water is gulped constantly and excess salts are excreted.

Fish senses, too, are strictly aquatic. Fishes are adapted to see and pick up sound vibrations in liquid rather than in air. The sense of smell functions by way of a double set of nostrils that sample the water as it flows in and then out. Fishes also have a unique sense, the lateral line system. This consists of nerve cells lining skin canals that are distributed over the head and body. By means of the lateral line, fishes can accurately gauge water flow and pressure, a vitally important ability in their environment.

The "In Between" Amphibians

Amphibians can be considered fence straddlers as far as a zone of adaptation is concerned. This group, composed of salamanders, frogs, and toads, appears to hover between water and land. On the one hand, they have limbs for walking on solid ground, lungs or specialized skin for breathing air, and a sensory system that is keyed to seeing and hearing on land. Yet for breeding most of them return to the water, where the young develop. Even for just plain living they all require a great deal of moisture to be really comfortable. But, from another point of view, amphibians can be thought of as perfectly well adapted to their particular zone, which is the habitat provided by any moist and wet condition on the ground or in bushes and trees.

It is generally misleading to consider the

Salamanders (opposite page) also have to breed in water. Notice their eggs attached to under-water vegetation.

The male tree frog (right) is inflating his throat pouch to croak. The croaking attracts female frogs. The male and female tree frog must go to a body of water to breed.

32

Toads (above) are power-ful swimmers; they use their back legs for extra push. Mating takes place in the water, where the toad's eggs are laid.

developmental stages of an individual to be a recapitulation of its ancestry through time. But the metamorphosis, or change-over, from a finned and gilled aquatic larva or tadpole to a four-limbed, air-breathing adult sala-mander or frog is very reminiscent of the evolutionary path undergone by the first amphibians.

A group of fish called lobe-fins are believed to be the ancestors of the first vertebrates to go on land. Pectoral and pelvic fins became front and hind legs respectively. These were attached to the spinal column by bony gir-dles. The spine became a strongly articulated but still flexible girder for bearing the weight of the body.

It is believed that land vertebrates origi-nated during what was, ironically, an at-tempt to stay within the old adaptive zone of fishes; that is, water. As pools dried out during the drought-stricken Devonian period (some 300 million years ago), lobe-finned fishes dragged themselves over land for longer and longer periods in order to reach still-filled bodies of water. Eventually, some of them were so well adapted for land locomotion that they forged the beginnings of the amphibians, feeding on early insects and spiders that had already colonized the land.

The earliest amphibians seem to have had fishlike scales. Most later forms, however, developed naked, moist skins, lubricated by means of inner glands. The moist skin is necessary for oxygen and carbon dioxide exchange; even though they have lungs, the skin is a very important additional breathing mechanism for amphibians.

The amphibian's circulatory system is more complex than the simple cycle of fishes. There are the beginnings of the double loop system. This system, so characteristic of the more advanced birds and mammals, keeps oxygenated blood from the lungs separate from depleted blood returning from the internal organs. In amphibians, however, although the heart has two separate chambers for returning blood, there is only one for pumping the blood out again. Thus some mixing does take place.

In their own way, amphibians are a very successful group, numbering some three thousand species.

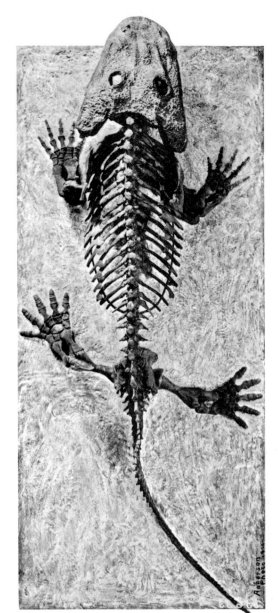

The skeleton (left) is a fossil of an amphibian, Eryops, *that lived about 350 million years ago. It was about five feet long and had a heavy body and flat skull. The* Eryops *fossil has helped scientists trace the evolutionary pattern from fish to the modern salamander (below right).*

Xenopus, *the frog shown below at left, must always stay in water. The small curved claws are unusual for an amphibian like this.*

Reptiles and Land

A fully land-adapted vertebrate did not arrive on the evolutionary scene until the first reptile laid its shelled egg on soil. The development of land reproduction broke the amphibian tie to water and opened the way to full exploitation of the terrestrial habitat.

The developing reptile embryo, like fish and amphibian embryos, is surrounded by liquid. But this liquid is contained within membranes and a leathery, limy shell. The shell protects the embryo from drying up. Thus the eggs can be laid on land.

A reptile has solid land legs that raise its body somewhat more off the ground than do the limbs of amphibians. However, in most cases, the legs are still positioned at an awkward angle sideways to the body.

This tortoise (right) lives on land. It carries the weight of its heavy shell on thick legs. Other turtle species live entirely in the water.

Monitors (below) are the largest of the modern lizards. Some reach a length of ten feet. They have a very long history: species very much like this one flourished about 50 million years ago.

Unlike the always moist amphibians, reptiles have dry skin, constructed of a leathery and scaly outer layer that has very few glands and that serves to hold in the body fluids. Along with fish and amphibians, reptiles are cold-blooded. This somewhat misleading term does not imply that these animals are particularly cold. What it does mean is that their body temperatures are dependent on the condition of the water or air that surrounds them, and that they have no internal physiological mechanism for keeping body

temperatures constant. Unlike fish and amphibians, reptiles perform best at relatively high body temperatures; muscular coordination and movement, the digestion of food, and reproductive processes are all inhibited at low temperatures. To attain adequately high levels, the reptilian solution is not physiological, but behavioral. They seek out warm rocks to lie on or direct sunshine in which to bask, thus raising their internal temperature. To cool off, they retreat into the shade or underground.

The chameleon (above) looks like a prehistoric animal. It is very well adapted for life in trees. The chameleon can change colors to blend with its surroundings.

The shingleback lizard of Australia (left) has an unusual but effective way of frightening its enemies. It opens its mouth showing its bright blue tongue against a crimson background.

37

The first reptiles evolved some 300 million years ago. They soon became the dominant land forms. Some of them even returned to an aquatic existence. Their heyday lasted until the end of the Mesozoic era (about 90 million years ago). Then, for still unknown reasons, their most impressive and most highly specialized representatives, the dinosaurs, became extinct.

Reptiles are still quite successful animals. But today they inhabit only a relatively minor portion of the earth's ecological niches. They include the turtles, lizards, snakes, and crocodilians.

The breathing of reptiles is much more efficient for land purposes than the gulping of air or gaseous exchange through the skin practiced by amphibians. Reptiles use only lungs, with the air being pumped in and out by muscles located around the rib cage.

Reptile senses, too, are very well suited to out-of-water functioning. The middle-ear mechanism, including the eardrum, was already present in amphibians. But in reptiles it is better equipped for amplifying sound waves. The waves, in turn, energize liquid-soaked nerve endings located deep within the skull. Land vision is well provided for by protective eyelids and lubricating fluids that keep sensitive eyes moist and functional even in dry surroundings.

All the modifications in structure that fit the reptiles for a land existence would be useless without the development of appropriate behavior. This, in turn, depends on the structure of the nervous system. The reptilian brain is more advanced than that of fishes and amphibians. It has the beginnings of higher centers in the forebrain that integrate overall activity. In the lower vertebrates there are only separate centers, with each center related to a special sense organ.

Snakes and lizards have many differences but they belong to the same order. Snakes are actually descended from lizard ancestors. During the course of evolution snakes lost their legs and developed long, narrow bodies.

The South American armadillo lizard (right) has a built-in defense against enemies. It coils up with its spiny tail in its mouth. In this way its soft underside is protected.

The cobra (opposite page) releases a deadly poison through its fangs. This poison is both a defense and a means of killing prey.

Into the Air

Birds have aptly been called feathered reptiles because in many ways they are still quite close to their scaly reptilian forebears. Yet, it is the possession of those very feathers that make birds the unique group that they are. The change-over from scales to feathers as a skin covering is tied to birds being warm-blooded vertebrates capable of flight. And, everything about these fliers reflects their basic zone of adaptation, the aerial way of life.

Flying requires a kind of long-lasting energy and a lightness of body construction, neither of which typical reptiles possess. Warm-bloodedness, or the maintenance of a constant internal heat level independent of changes in the environment, has been attained through a high rate of metabolism or bodily functioning. The highly efficient circulatory and respiratory systems of birds are needed to maintain this high rate of metabolism. Blood has to be well aerated and the tissues constantly supplied with new food and oxygen at the same time that waste products are carried off.

Feathers function not only as insulation, retaining the body's heat, but also as efficient aerofoils during flight. In addition, downy feathers serve as a nest lining.

To lighten the skeleton, many of the bones are hollow. Instead of ponderous toothed jaws, a light but effective horny beak man-

Feathers are very important during flight. They also insulate the bird's body. For the breeding season some birds, like the male egret (above), grow additional plumage that attracts female birds.

Toucans (left) can be recognized easily by their bright colors and large beaks. The beaks are very light-weight and do not hinder flight.

The structure of a bird's beak varies with its feeding habits. The saddle-billed stork (above) finds food such as frogs in shallow river basins. Its beak is suited for pulling the prey from mud.

The fierce-looking eagle (left) is a native of tropical forests. Monkeys form the major part of his diet. With his strong, sharply hooked bill he can easily tear meat apart.

41

ages food. The breastbone is no longer flat as in reptiles but carries a deep keel for the attachment of powerful flight muscles leading to the arms. The rib cage is reinforced to hold it together during the strain of flight; the bony girdle to which the legs are hinged is fused very firmly to the vertebral column.

In the large brain, those centers that control muscular coordination and balance are especially well developed. So, too, are the centers that are related to instinctual activities; much of the marvelously intricate behavior of birds is fixed from birth, rather than learned by experience.

Prolonged care of the young after hatching is a major aspect of behavior that has been added by birds to the reptilian reproduction process.

There are over 8,000 species of birds in the world. Some birds are solitary creatures. Others, like the murres (opposite page), live and breed in large colonies.

Skimmers (above) can be found near water in the warmer parts of the world. These birds skim the waves in search of food.

An owl (left) has very soft feathers. These do not make any noise as the owl flies through night skies in search of prey.

43

The Progressive Mammals

It is difficult to think of a fish out of water. A frog far from the pond's margin also seems incongruous. And, although there are flightless birds, they are an oddity. Mammals, on the other hand, even though their progress over the reptile level of organization has been primarily in terms of refined adaptations for land, have become, by the very nature of their physiological advance, more independent of their immediate surroundings.

The mammalian organization includes many features that together enable life to be supported under conditions that appear "difficult." For example, a camel and the man who rides it through the desert contain more water than the air and sandy wastes for miles around. This is possible because of the kind of waterproofing and elaborate storage systems of the warm mammalian body.

The ability to maintain a high and constant body temperature has opened to mammals (and birds) many habitats closed to reptiles. Mammals attained their temperature-regulation system independently from that evolved by birds. Although both groups have developed the kind of blood and oxygen distribution system necessary to maintain their high metabolic rate, they have each assembled their systems in different anatomical fashion. An analogy would be two differ-

Many mammals have adapted to special habitats. Dolphins (above), for example, have evolved as water dwellers. Baboons (right), on the other hand, are monkeys that live on land rather than in trees.

ently constructed engines both capable of delivering similar amounts of power. Instead of the feathers of birds, mammals have hair for heat insulation. Both groups have separate circulatory cycles for aerated and deoxygenated blood, and both groups have highly efficient lungs. In mammals, the lungs function on a bellows system in which not only the rib cage but also a muscular sheet, the diaphragm, takes part.

The really essential mammalian hallmark is the development of the forebrain, or cerebral cortex. No other animal group depends so much on this all-important coordinating and integrating center to respond to environmental stimuli.

Cheetahs, like all the cats, are beautifully adapted to life on land. With strong muscles and powerful jaws and teeth, they are skilled hunters.

Mammals first evolved some 170 million years ago. The main changes from their reptile ancestors that can be observed in fossil skeletons consist of changes in their jaws and teeth, as well as in the limbs. Teeth, instead of being similar throughout the mouth, became differentiated into the kinds of ripping, stabbing, cutting, and grinding teeth today's mammals possess. The lower jaw, instead of being composed of many bones, as in fishes, amphibians, and reptiles, changed into a single more solid, bony strut. All these jaw and tooth changes resulted in a more efficient method of chewing food—which again relates to a heightened way of living.

Changes in the limbs were all in the direction of pulling the legs up under the body. Thus, instead of the crawling, sideways sprawl of reptiles, the true mammalian fore and aft stride during locomotion became possible. In consequence, the mammal stands high on its legs when it moves.

Another big mammalian advance is the mode of reproduction. With few exceptions, the embryos develop within the mother's body. During their embryonic existence, most are nourished by food drawn from the mother's blood stream. After birth the young are fed milk. There is usually an extensive period of care and training by one or both parents. Unlike the birds, mammals display fewer instinctive responses to their surroundings, and the early learning period is essential to their lives.

Mammals are found in all parts of the world and in every kind of environment. Some idea of the variety among mammals is shown on these two pages.

American badgers (opposite page) can be found from southwestern Canada to central Mexico. Badgers are champion burrowers. They can dig their way underground in seconds.

Elephant shrews (top) live in Africa. Some are forest animals. They hide under logs and dead leaves, nibbling such food as insects and bird eggs.

Bats (left) are the only flying mammals. They can be found all over the world. Bats are nocturnal, often sheltering in caves. Most are insect-eaters.

The huge African buffalo (below) are the most dangerous African game animals. These buffalo live near water and grass. They use nearby trees for shade.

The Business of Living

Feeding

Everything that lives must eat.

The eating habits of animals vary greatly. This tends to provide a balance that guarantees abundance for all. Some animals specialize in eating leaves or grass or grain. Some eat other animals. Each kind has its own means of procuring, chewing, and digesting food that is best suited to its needs. In no case does any one group of animals, with the possible exception of man, ever seriously deplete its source of food.

Great hunters can be found in every class of animals. The shark about to snap at another fish (above) and the dining lion (right) are extremely skilled hunters. Although they survive on the flesh of other vertebrates, they eat only as much as they need.

Eagles are beautifully
equipped birds of prey.
Their hooked bill is
ideal for tearing flesh.
Their strong feet,
with sharp, curved claws,
grasp and tear the
prey. Their sharp eye-
sight is equal to that of a
man with binoculars.
Finally, eagles have long
wings, helping them to
soar for hours as
their eyes sweep the
ground for food.

49

The Meat-Eaters. The business of meat-eating is somewhat more complicated than that of plant-eating. Vegetation is readily available in most parts of the world; the animal feeding upon it has simply to wander about nibbling at random. Meat-eaters must put in somewhat more effort to find their food. This is particularly true of animals that prefer a diet of other living vertebrates—in other words, the hunters.

Hunters must have highly acute senses for locating their prey. They must have enough speed and agility to run down the prey. Most important of all, the hunter must be more intelligent than the life it hunts. It is this superior intelligence that makes these animals particularly interesting to mankind.

Each class of vertebrates has its hunters. Most fish hunt and eat each other. Anyone keeping tropical fish in an aquarium can

A hunter must have sharp senses, persistence, and more intelligence than his victim. The owl (above) depends as much on his sense of hearing as on vision. Speed, silence, and deadly accuracy ensure the kill for this bird of prey.

A bear (right) eats a lot of food. It eats both plant food and meat. Bears have teeth suited to a varied diet rather than to straight meat-eating.

50

Like all vultures, the griffon vultures shown here are scavengers. Despite their large size, they never kill. They are content with the meat of animals already dead—known as carrion —rather than with fresh meat. Vultures are often scorned, but they are necessary for maintaining sanitation. When they have finished with this zebra, the tiny pieces of meat left on the bones will be quickly eaten by other scavengers, such as carrion-eating beetles.

appreciate the predatory nature of these small vertebrates. But of all the watery hunters, sharks seem particularly well-equipped. The sleek figure of the shark and the silence with which it glides through the waters make its presence ever ominous.

Among reptiles, crocodiles are notorious killers. So, too, are snakes. They do so much to keep down the rodent population that, in many tropical locations, they are kept as household pets.

As for the birds, eagles and hawks are particularly amazing to watch at their work. From hundreds of feet in the air, they swoop down on their prey with marksmanship any bombardier would envy.

In the mammal group, the big cats (tigers, lions, pumas, and cheetahs) are champion hunters. They have all the skill and patience necessary to the game. The little weasel, for his size, is an unparalleled killer, as are his cousins, the bigger wolverines. And wolves and wild dogs are well known for their terrifyingly efficient pack-hunting techniques.

Most fish are meat-eaters. Big fish usually eat smaller ones, including members of their own species. The pike below is swallowing another pike. Frequently baby fish are eaten by their parents.

For a leopard (opposite page), catching and killing prey is only part of the job. He must also find privacy in which to eat. In this case, the best place seems to be high in a tree. The leopard's great strength is demonstrated by the fact that he has been able to haul this antelope up so far.

A hunter that lives in the sea is built quite differently from a land-hunter or skydiver. But all have certain features in common. Sharks and cats have powerful muscular bodies, built for maximum speed. Snakes and weasels are suited for the quick, darting movement that takes prey completely unprepared. The sharp, cutting teeth of cats is matched in birds of prey with an equally sharp bill. In every part of the environment, the hunters are there, beautifully equipped to do the job of holding nature's balance intact.

Eaters of Insects and Worms. Many eaters of meat content themselves with smaller game than other vertebrates. These animals have found that the supply of protein available in the form of invertebrates such as insects and earthworms is far more abundant and easier to come by. For this way of life, an animal must have a different sort of equip-

ment than that found in the big-game hunters. While the senses must be acute, sharp cutting teeth are not as necessary a requisite. Any method of catching, holding, and then gulping down the prey will do.

Insect-eaters appear in every class of vertebrates. Many fish dart at insects and worms —a fact on which fishermen depend.

Most amphibians are oriented toward small flying and crawling things. The frog has a specially built tongue that is attached at the front of the mouth and flips out with great speed and marksmanship when a fly is available.

Among reptiles, lizards are particularly good at catching and ridding the world of insects. Most turtles like worms; nor will they pass up a fly or beetle if it is unwary enough to approach closely.

The smaller birds are certainly great eaters of insects. This fact was emphasized when recent sprayings of insecticides killed off

Insects are an easy
source of protein to ob-
tain. Many small animals
eat insects. The giant
anteater of South
America (right) also eats
insects. Usually it is
not practical for such
a large animal to de-
pend on insects for food.
The anteater, however,
is perfectly adapted to
his way of life. His front
paws are powerfully
clawed for digging into
nests. His tongue, which
extends about eight
inches from his snout,
is very sticky. Each time
the anteater sticks his
tongue into termite tun-
nels, it comes out with
hundreds of insects
glued to it.

The frog (opposite page,
top) uses his tongue to
catch insects and worms.
Frogs are among our
most valuable insect
exterminators. They rid
the world of a large
number of pests.

Lizards (opposite page,
bottom) are also insect
eaters. Here, a beetle provides a hearty meal
for its captor.

54

thousands of the best-loved songbirds.

Many mammals are insect-eaters. Most bats catch flying insects for food. Insects are also the chief food of shrews and moles. Some shrews eat twice their own weight in insects every day!

Some mammals have specific adaptations for eating ants and termites. Usually, these include a long snout containing few, if any teeth, and a very long, sticky tongue that can be pushed into underground nests. Strong digging claws on the forefeet are generally also present. Anteating mammals include the Australian egglaying spiny anteater, the marsupial anteater, and several South American anteaters. The largest anteater measures some six feet in length—a surprising amount of bulk to be sustained by ants. But this animal is so well-endowed by nature for the gathering of ants that thousands of these insects may be taken in just a few moments. Armadillos are also quite fond of ants, although they will also eat many other foods.

Mankind owes a great debt to the insect-eaters; they help to maintain the balance of nature. If it weren't for the insect-eaters, insects might literally overrun the earth.

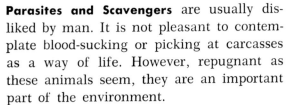

Parasites and Scavengers are usually disliked by man. It is not pleasant to contemplate blood-sucking or picking at carcasses as a way of life. However, repugnant as these animals seem, they are an important part of the environment.

Lampreys and hag fishes are parasites. These fish attach themselves, by means of their sucker mouths, to other fish, living off their substance. Vampire bats are also parasites. These mammals suck the blood of other warm-blooded vertebrates.

The scavengers include vultures, patrolling the skies in search of death, and hyenas, renowned for eating garbage.

The animals mentioned above are anatomically suited to this specific way of life. There are, besides, many hunting animals that do not disdain carrion when it is available. A fish, turtle, hawk, or dog that finds a large hunk of meat in its path, in the form of a corpse, will eat it. This is a piece of good luck not to be ignored.

The Plant-Eaters.

There are plants everywhere on earth. In the hot, sandy desert, one finds cactus growing. Even in the frigid Arctic there are lichens growing on the rocks. Beneath the ice of the sea, there is floating greenery. The variety is staggering: from microscopic aquatic algae to the huge trees of the forest and the thousands of species in between. And almost all of them grow in abundance; given the proper soil and water, plus sunlight, they thrive.

This abundance of vegetation has been utilized by many kinds of vertebrates. Every kind of plant is eaten by one kind of animal or another. As the diversity of plants is so great, the eaters of them are also highly diverse, with special adaptations that suit each for its chosen diet. The tiny humming-bird feeding on nectar and the large trunked elephant breaking off branches have little in common, but both are dependent on vegetation and have evolved anatomies suitable to their respective diets.

Plant-eaters can be distinguished from meat-eaters by anatomy and behavior. While meat-eaters have sharp cutting teeth, plant-eaters have heavy grinding teeth or special bills. Because plant-eaters acquire their food in a passive rather than an aggressive manner, their bodies conform to their habits; they are built for defense rather than offense.

Each of the animals on these pages has a different kind of diet. This helps assure abundance for all.

The legless lizard (opposite page, top) eats various insects.

The spiny anteater, or echidna (opposite page, bottom), is an egg-laying mammal. It feeds on Australian termites.

The lamprey (opposite page, right) is a primitive fish. It attaches itself to other fish with a suction-cup mouth. Using horny rasps, it digs its way inside, where it drains the body fluids of its victim.

The large deer (top) and the tiny mouse (bottom) are both plant-eaters, but the deer concentrates on grass and leaves while the mouse prefers grain and seeds.

Just as there are meat-eaters in every category of vertebrate, there are also plant-eaters of every class. Plant-eaters have to take in a larger volume of food to provide them with the necessary energy to exist, so usually more time is spent eating and digesting than is the case in meat-eaters.

While many fish eat meat, there are also many that live on vegetation. There is some plant matter in all water. Even a still, polluted-looking mud hole is covered with green slime. That slime is actually millions of tiny plants, clustered together, that are commonly referred to as algae. Many fish, in both fresh and salt waters, live on algae.

Young frog and toad tadpoles also eat aquatic vegetation. As they grow larger, however, their need for protein increases and they become more meat-dependent.

Turtles that live in the water also feed on

Hummingbirds sip nectar from flowers. They are well equipped for this activity. Their wings can beat very rapidly (as many as 50 vibrations per second). Thus the hummingbird can hover almost motionless over its food. It can also flit from flower to flower quickly, taking as much nectar as it wants. The nectar clings to the brushlike tip of its long tongue.

aquatic vegetation. Those on land eat all sorts of plants, including many that grow in our gardens.

Many mammals are dependent on plants for their food. Rodents eat grain and nuts, rabbits eat vegetables, rhinos browse on leaves, and cows eat grass.

In fact, there is a whole group of fairly large-sized mammals that live on grass. They are called "ruminants" for their special handling of this food. Grass is not easy to digest. Ruminants such as goats, sheep, cattle, antelopes, and deer have compartmentalized stomachs to aid them in digestion. But there are many mammals without this advantage that also eat grass. Among these are horses and kangaroos.

Some mammals are browsers rather than grazers (rhinos, tapirs, and elephants are just a few). They eat leaves, twigs, and buds rather than hard grass. The grinding teeth of these animals are not as modified as those of the grass-eaters.

Vampire bats are well known for their nasty habits. But very little is ever said about the gentle and charming fruit bats. These mammals suck out the juice of such lush

Like birds, bats are able to fly to their food. Fruit bats (above) have a fringed tongue like that of a hummingbird. They use the tongue to remove the juice and pulp from their favorite food.

Rabbits eat a wide variety of plants. A pest to most truck farmers, rabbits eat many of the same vegetables we enjoy. They are well-equipped for their diet. They have sharp teeth in the front of their mouth for tearing and strong molars behind for grinding.

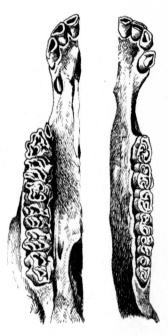

plants as figs, dates, guavas, and mangoes.

Even those mammals most closely related to man, the apes, are mostly vegetarians. Generally, they disdain animal food. More like man in dietary habits are the bears and raccoons. These animals vary their diets to include some meat and some vegetables, thereby enjoying all that nature has to offer.

Some of the specializations found among the plant-eating animals are truly astonishing. This is particularly true among vegetarian birds and mammals. The bill of a parrot, for instance, is very powerful. It is hinged to the skull in such a way that tremendous leverage can be developed for crushing large and hard seeds.

Those other great seed-eaters, the mice, have front teeth that grow constantly as they wear down. Also, these teeth are sharpened against each other to form an ever-sharp chisel, which operates most effectively against seed casings. Hummingbirds have a structure very much like a ball and socket joint at the shoulder. This permits them to hover "motionless" in mid-air while sipping nectar from a flower. Also, these birds have very long tongues with brushlike tips.

Fruit bats obtain pulp and juice from fruit

Horses (opposite page) eat grass, a plant that is difficult to chew. The strong ridges and crests in the horse's teeth (above) make them ideal grinding tools.

The cuscus (above left), a marsupial of Australia and nearby regions, is a tree-dweller. Consequently, it eats what it finds there: mainly fruits, leaves, and insects but also birds and bird's eggs.

in several ways. Some use their tongues to extract the pulp; others suck or chew it. After swallowing the juice, they spit out the dry mash and seeds. Some fruit bats have a special structure of the lips, windpipe, and gullet that forms a suction mechanism for drawing in the fruit pulp.

The swallow-tanager has a hooked bill with sharp edges that works well in cutting up fruit. But it prefers to swallow its food whole. The bird has a pouch, capable of

Deer (above) and yaks (opposite page, bottom) are members of a mammal group called ruminants. The stomach of a ruminant is divided into compartments. Bacteria in the stomach break down the grasses eaten by the animal into easily digestible matter.

There are thousands of species of plants. Most of them are eaten by some kind of animal. Dormice (right) eat nuts, buds, and leaves. The crow (opposite page, top) is one of many animals that enjoys berries. Crows also eat grain, making them a prime target for farmers.

stretching a long way, beneath its bill.

Pocket gophers also have pouches for holding food. In their case, these extend from the cheeks clear back to the shoulders. The gophers' diet consists of dirt-covered roots and stems, on which they gnaw while in their underground burrows. Their lips can close tightly behind their front teeth, so that dirt does not enter the mouth while they are gnawing.

Manatees are strict vegetarians. They feed on aquatic plants and land plants that overhang the water. A manatee's upper lip is split to be used as a forceps for picking up food; heavy bristles on the muzzle help push plants into the mouth.

During the berry season, when the smell of ripe fruit is heavy in the air, even the most confirmed meat-eater may be tempted to join the plant-eaters for a meal or two. As a matter of fact, many ordinarily carnivorous animals gladly supplement their diets with plant food, which is often more readily obtainable than meat.

Breeding

Life began in the sea. Thus the kind of reproduction that takes place in water represents the earliest form of reproduction. Most fish breed in the same way that fish have bred for millions of years. Amphibians, the first land vertebrates, must still return to the water to breed. It is here that we find their eggs and the emerging tadpoles.

To survive as an individual, an animal must eat enough food to maintain itself. The survival of a species depends on reproduction. The greater the success in producing offspring, the more dominant the group becomes.

If an animal is unhealthy through lack of the proper foods, he is unlikely to breed. Or, if he does, he is likely to have weaker offspring. But providing that all the requirements for a healthy life are met, there are still obstacles to breeding that must be overcome. Many breeding problems are encountered in the various environments in which animals live; each must be solved in a different way. The methods worked out to accommodate new life are many. In general,

however, they can be broken down into four categories: egg-laying in water, egg-laying on land, live birth in water, and live birth on land.

Egg-Laying in Water. Backboned animals began their history in water; and egg-laying in water is the oldest form of reproduction practiced and perfected by vertebrates.

Fish that live in cold environments have breeding seasons. Those that live in the tropics may breed at any time of the year. Some fish lay floating eggs. Others have sticky eggs that become attached to plants. Others bury eggs beneath soil or gravel at the bottom.

Most fish eggs, whatever the environment, have a yolk. The developing embryo feeds on the yolk until hatching and, in some instances, a long while afterward. The young

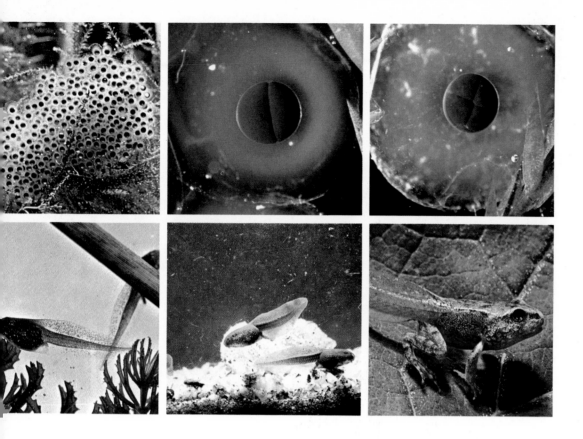

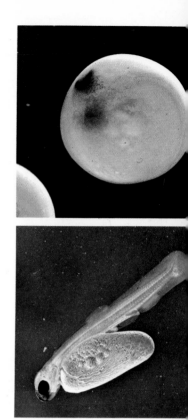

fish are known as larvae. This means that they must undergo certain changes before they fully resemble their parents. In some cases the larvae look so different that even an expert has difficulty identifying them.

There are intricate courtship rituals in some species of fish. Other species seem quite casual about the whole thing. In most cases, at the right moment, the female will drop her unfertilized eggs near the waiting male, who covers them with sperm.

Amphibians have adapted very well to life on humid land in all respects but one: the vast majority of them must return to water to breed. Frogs and toads usually congregate at a body of water at mating season. The males croak their own funny song to attract the females. After pairing off, the male climbs on the back of the female, clasping her tightly around her middle with his arms. In this manner, they swim around until the female is ready to lay her eggs. She stretches out her hind legs; the eggs emerge at the same time that the male releases his sperm.

Most male salamanders have beautiful breeding colors and special scent glands with which to attract females. The male presents the female with a bundle of sperm wrapped in a jellylike capsule, which the female inserts into her vent. The female then lays eggs that have been fertilized by the sperm inside her body.

Amphibian eggs may be laid in clusters on the surface of the water or among the leaves of aquatic plants.

In general, aquatic eggs are laid in great numbers; only a very small percentage survive to develop into a new generation.

Above left, in the top row from left to right: (a) an amphibian egg mass in the water. Each gelatinous capsule contains a single cell, the fertilized egg. (b) An egg cell that has split in two. (c) The same egg at the four-cell stage. In the bottom row from left to right: (d) two tadpoles have hatched from their gelatinous membranes. (e) A tadpole that is beginning to develop hind legs. (f) An almost completely adult frog. Only the tail remains to be absorbed.

Above right: a trout egg and hatched trout larva still with yolk sac attached. The larva does not feed independently until the yolk sac has been absorbed.

65

Egg-Laying On Land. The first land eggs were laid by the early reptiles. This made reptiles the first group of vertebrates to be fully terrestrial. The reptilian egg contains the embryo and a large supply of yolk for nourishment. A leathery casing, the shell, surrounds and protects the developing embryo and the yolk from drying out.

Most reptiles do not build elaborate nests. Generally, the eggs are simply deposited on the ground and a little earth or sand is scratched over them. Turtles use their hind feet to dig gourd-shaped holes into which the eggs are deposited. Crocodilians heap plant debris mixed with soil over their clutch.

A clutch of eggs may number from under ten to more than one hundred, depending on the species. In most cases, it is the heat of the sun that incubates the reptilian egg. However, certain lizards and snakes will coil themselves around their eggs for protection and to provide some warmth.

When the young reptiles emerge, they are fully active individuals and look very much like their parents. To aid in breaking the

Reptiles were the first animals to lay eggs on land. The dinosaur eggs (opposite page) have been fossilized. They show the same kind of structure as modern reptile eggs such as those of the turtle (near and far left) and the lizard (above).

The platypus (right) is a monotreme. These are reptilelike mammals found in Australia and New Zealand. Instead of bearing live young, these unusual mammals lay eggs. After the young have hatched, however, care is typically mammalian. The young are carefully protected and fed with milk from the mother's body.

shell, each young reptile has a small "egg tooth" on its snout. This tooth disappears shortly after the reptile hatches.

Fertilization in reptiles is always internal. The male and female intertwine their tails, bringing the two vents into opposition.

Even those reptiles that live in the water return to land to lay their eggs. However, for these aquatic reptiles, such as crocodiles and certain turtles, courtship and mating take place in the water. Breeding can be a pretty violent affair among crocodiles. The aggressive males roar and bellow; on mating, a male sometimes bites the female severely in the neck.

Mating in snakes is much more peaceful. The male and female maneuver their bodies to make internal fertilization possible. A few male snakes have vestiges of hind legs; with these, a male scratches the female's sides as he slides over her back.

Birds also lay eggs on land. Their eggs contain more calcium in the shell and are more rigid than the reptilian eggs. The birds use the warmth of their own always heated bodies to incubate the embryos inside the eggs. This has led to a great variety of nesting techniques.

Nests can be woven out of twigs, grass, fur, or feathers. Or they can be shallow depressions in the ground. Some birds dig tunnels; others use mud or saliva with which to build homes.

Courtship and mating in birds are as

Bird eggs (top) have more calcium in the shell than reptile eggs. This adds hardness to the bird eggs.

The bird (center), with its fossilized egg, was an elephant bird. This species once lived on Madagascar. It reached a height of 9 feet and laid eggs weighing 18 pounds.

varied as nesting habits. There are birds that are polygamous (several females to one male), birds that are polyandrous (several males to one female), birds that pair for one breeding season, and those that mate for life.

Most male birds have exquisite plumage they "show off" during courtship rituals that vary from species to species.

After mating, males may take an active part in nest-building and incubation or they may be completely indifferent. In polygamous birds, the males usually ignore the young, but care for the females. Polyandrous females leave the males to look after the eggs; the females go off to find new mates.

Bird eggs may be round, oval, or pyramid-shaped. They are sometimes white, but more frequently are colored. The emerging infants may be naked and helpless on hatching or fully feathered and ready to leave the nest.

Most amphibians lay their eggs and swim away. The midwife toad (bottom, far left) is an exception. The male midwife toad attaches the fertilized eggs to his thighs. He keeps the eggs with him until they hatch.

Among most birds, the female takes care of the eggs. The female plover (below) will sit on her eggs to keep them warm.

A new-born shark (right) takes his first swim through the water. Most fish hatch from eggs, but sharks are born live.

Live Birth in Water. Although most fish lay eggs, some species give birth to live off-spring. Most notable of these are the sharks and rays. Other, smaller, species also do this. Guppies and mollies, the very popular aquarium fish, have tiny live offspring as do many of the perchlike fish.

Most live-bearing mother fish simply retain the eggs within the body. Here, the young are nourished by the yolk until they are ready to hatch. But some fish have eggs with no yolk; the developing embryos must be nourished by food from the mother's body.

The group that is best known for internal development, live birth, and later feeding of milk by the mother are the mammals. One does not usually think of these animals as courting and reproducing in water, but there are several that do.

Whales live their entire lives in the sea. They court, mate, and have their young in the water they call home. Among sperm whales, the harem situation is usual, with each male allied with several females. Those whales frequenting cold waters swim to warmer parts of the world when the young are ready to be born. The young are quite

Some ancient reptiles lived in the water. They were fishlike in appearance. They did not lay their eggs on land; the mother kept the eggs in her body until they hatched. The fossil ichthyosaur (above), preserved in limestone, was a female with young inside her body cavity about to be born.

Dolphins (right), like most mammals, bear live young. The young can manage well in the water from the time of their birth; they need just a little assistance from their mother.

large, usually about half as big as the mother, and are born underwater. Mother whales usually push their newborn infants to the surface for their first breath of air. When ready to nurse, the mother lies on her side in the water, so the baby is close to the surface and can breathe. A fold of skin around the nipple forms a sort of valve for blocking out the surrounding water, while the baby nurses. Whale's milk is about four times as rich as cow's milk, so the young grow very rapidly.

Sea otters also have live young in the water. A single pup is born at a very advanced stage of development, with eyes open and a full set of milk teeth, enabling it to take soft food almost from birth. Nevertheless, it nurses for almost a year. The mother floats on her back while nursing the pup.

Dugongs and manatees, frequently referred to as sea cows, are also mammals that bear their live young in the water. Dugongs have a single offspring, born underwater, which is pushed to the surface for air. Manatees are affectionate animals, especially during the mating season. The female bears a single calf, which is fed underwater in a horizontal position.

The shark shown above has just given birth to live young. In a few moments these young fish will be actively swimming through the water, small replicas of their parents.

Baboons (right), like most mammals, give birth to well-developed offspring. Child care is prolonged until the young are almost fully mature.

Half-grown opossum babies (below) dangle from their mother's pouch. They crawled there when they were the size of bumblebees. Here they remain, attached to their mother's nipples, until strong enough to be on their own.

The baby proboscis monkey (below, right) will need his mother for a long time. He is too helpless to survive on his own.

Live Birth on Land.

When we speak of live birth on land, we think first of the mammals, for, indeed, these are the dominant land animals. There are, however, amphibians and reptiles that give birth on land to live young.

The advantages of live birth over eggs are obvious. All during their development the newborn have been protected from climate and predators by the mother's body.

Among the amphibians, there is a species of salamander that lives in the Alps of Europe. It bears live young there in the melting snows.

Some lizards and snakes also have live young. Viper babies, carried within the mother's body until they hatch from their eggs, already have enough venom in their fangs to kill several rodents. Cottonmouths and copperheads are also live-bearers. So, too, are sea snakes; they go to small crevices in the rocks on near-by islands to bear their young.

However, it is the mammals that have best evolved the business of live birth on land. Through the possession of a special structure known as a placenta, mother mammals are able to feed their young internally until they are fairly mature. Blood passes from the mother to the embryo through the placenta. Although the placenta is best developed in mammals, other animals—such as some of the fish and reptiles we have discussed—have modified placentas.

Two groups of mammals do not have placentas. Members of one of these, the monotremes, lay eggs. The others, the marsupials, have young at a very immature stage. The young are then carried attached to the mother's nipples, often in a pouch.

Mammals, generally do not have elaborate courting rituals. Smaller mammals make nests, but with none of the versatility that one finds in birds.

The reproductive area in which the mammals truly excel is in child care after birth.

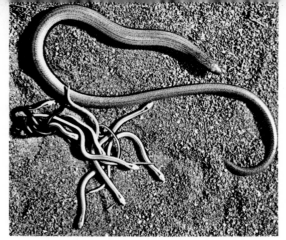

Many different kinds of land animals bear live young. Most reptiles lay eggs, but there are livebearing snakes (left). Some seals (below) travel hundreds of miles to well-established breeding areas on land or ice. The halfgrown rabbits (below, far left) have reached a stage where their eyes are open and they can run. The newborn colt (bottom) is born well-developed.

Most lizards are indifferent to their offspring. The young lizard sitting on the adult's head (right) is probably there by accident.

Alligators (below) build mound nests that protect the developing eggs. Then they stay in the area. When they hear the call of the newly hatched young, they come to help free them from the nest.

Caring for the Young

Most fish do not spend a great deal of time caring for their young. Usually they lay thousands of eggs, then swim away and forget about them. Because of the large number of eggs, some are bound to survive. If all did, there would be an overpopulation problem in the seas.

There are, however, some species of fish that do care for their young. Several species, including such popular aquarium pets as cichlids and certain catfish, are mouthbreeders. Eggs are picked up by either the male or female and held in the mouth until they hatch. The parent does not eat for the entire duration of incubation. Once hatched, the young may remain in the parent's mouth until they become too large to fit in it.

Other aquarium fish, like the betas and gouramis, make bubble nests for their eggs. The male produces the bubbles, using mucous from his mouth combined with air and water. This mass floats to the surface. The male parent will guard and repair it.

Male sea horses carry their young in a pouch on their bellies. At the proper moment, the father wraps his tail around a plant. With muscular spasms similar to labor contractions, he ejects the perfectly formed babies, one at a time, into the water.

There are many other examples of child

care among the fishes, but all of these are exceptions to the general rule of indifference.

Amphibians are also likely to ignore the eggs they have laid. Like fish, most amphibians lay a large number of eggs. Where there are fewer eggs, more attention is paid to their preservation.

In midwife toads, it is the male who cares for the eggs. He wraps the long string of eggs taken from his mate around his hind thighs. Thereafter, he cares for the eggs, carrying them with him as he feeds and bathes.

Certain female treefrogs have a pouch on the back which the male stuffs with the eggs, once they are fertilized. When the tadpoles have hatched, the female reaches up with her hind foot and carefully opens the slit of the pouch, so the larvae can escape.

Reptile parents, like fish and amphibians, are not overly devoted to their offspring. Turtles ignore their eggs completely, as do most lizards. However, the green lizard of Europe stays near her eggs until they hatch. Female skinks are very maternal, turning their eggs and wrapping themselves around their clutch. In some species the mother even stays with the hatched young, cleaning them regularly.

Baby alligators begin to croak as they hatch out of their eggs. The mother 'gator then returns to help them from the nest mound that she had constructed earlier.

Birds spend a lot of time and energy caring for their young. To satisfy their offsprings' huge appetites (above), birds may make hundreds of trips daily in search of food. In addition, baby birds cannot defend themselves and must be carefully guarded even when they are as well developed at hatching as ostriches (below, left) or ducks (below, right).

Birds (opposite page) must gather food for their young. In contrast, mammals feed their young with milk from their own bodies. The mammals shown here are the peccary (top), the zebra (right), and the scaly pangolin (below). The young pangolin is not nursing but hitching a ride on its mother's tail.

In these rare instances among fish, amphibians, and reptiles, parental care is never of very long duration. Birds, on the other hand, take care of the young over a long period of time, beginning with the elaborate nests and the eggs and ending with the fully-fledged offspring. In some cases, only the mother cares for the young. In other species, both parents are involved.

Such birds as fowl, ducks, and ostriches are well feathered and able to leave the nest at hatching. The ostrich father manages, in spite of his large harem and subsequent large numbers of offspring, to keep all the chicks in order and protect them against enemies.

Female ducks bear the entire burden of child-raising, bustling in front of the brood as they are led to and from the water.

Male and female geese and swans mate for life and care for their families jointly. Swan parents keep their babies with them for a year, frequently nestling them on their backs between their uplifted wings.

Song birds, pigeons, and birds of prey are all born naked and helpless. It takes weeks of careful nurturing before they are ready to leave the nest. Feeding goes on continuously, and vigilance against predators must be constant. In many cases the parents will deliberately attract the attention of enemies to lead them away from the nest.

In general, the best parental care is pro-

During the nursing period, mother and offspring must stay together. The mother shrew (below) leads her young in a single file line. The opossum (bottom, left) carries her young on her back. The mouse lemur (bottom, right) carries her young around her neck.

vided by mammals. Not only do they care for their young until they are almost mature, but they feed the young with milk from their own bodies. Even the egg-laying monotremes have special milk-producing glands for feeding the young after they have hatched.

Mammal milk is a complete food, containing protein, fat, sugar, and salt. The nursing time varies in the various species from a few weeks in a rodent to several years in an elephant. Mammal mothers stand, sit, or lie down while nursing, depending on the location of the teats. In some, like deer and horses, the teats are located toward the groin; apes and bats have them on the chest; cats and dogs have teats almost the whole length of the belly.

Among the pouched mammals, nursing is particularly important. Marsupial babies are born at a very immature stage. Opossum babies, for instance, are tiny and have only the use of their front legs. They manage to wriggle up to the mother's pouch, where each grasps a nipple in its mouth. The nipple then expands. The baby is attached until it is sufficiently mature to begin to venture out into the world.

In placental mammals, the time spent in nursing is proportionately shorter than

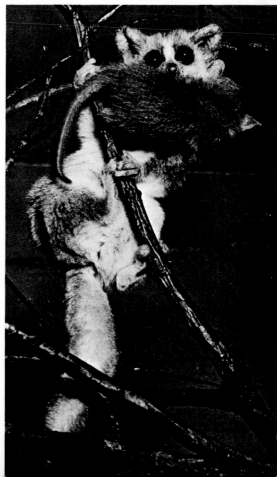

When a mother colugo goes to find food, she sometimes leaves her baby at home in its tree nest. There are times, however, when the baby must be taken along. Then it hangs on tightly to its mother's belly fur or nipples as *she* glides quickly from tree to tree.

among marsupials. However, nursing is still very important. Suckling is not constant but takes place at regular intervals.

Female bats of some species hibernate together in large clusters throughout the cold weather. Development of the egg from sperm stored the previous fall starts in warm weather. Each mother bears one child.

The offspring of plant-eaters learn rather quickly to take advantage of the abundant food at their disposal. Young meat-eaters have a more difficult time learning to catch prey. Frequently, adult hunters bring meat to their young and spend weeks teaching them how to hunt.

The greatest degree of family life is practiced by primates. In these animals parental care is long-enduring; several generations may live together in harmony. It has been said that the major reason for man's domination of the earth is the very long care and protection given the young by their parents.

Movement

Unlike plants, animals generally move about. They move from place to place in search of food. They also move to avoid their enemies.

Some animals are sessile, or attached to the ground or ocean floor. Even these animals will move, or agitate, their immediate environment by means of tentacles or other structures in order to provides themselves with food.

Vertebrates, in particular, excel in many kinds of locomotion. The well-developed

The sea turtle (top) uses its flippers for swimming. These are built like paddles, and the turtle "rows" itself along.

During swimming, the catfish (right) uses its fins for steering and balance. The tailfin, attached to the muscular tail, works like a vertical paddle. The paired side fins help the fish steer and balance itself. Unpaired fins along the back and underside prevent the catfish from tilting sideways.

muscles of their bodies enable them to fly like eagles, crawl like snakes, gallop like horses, waddle like ducks, or leap like porpoises.

Forms of locomotion vary from movement through water to movement on and above ground; from subterranean tunneling to tree-climbing, gliding, and true flight.

Swimming. Almost all vertebrates can swim if they have to. However, swimming ability varies from group to group. It depends largely on how much time an animal spends in the water. Whales and porpoises can swim as well and in some respects better than fish. Horses, dogs, and human beings do not swim as well; their muscles are not as well adapted for movement through water.

Most vertebrates use side-to-side movements when they swim. Even secondary swimmers, like crocodiles and salamanders, swim this way. The construction of the vertebral column and the muscles attached to it cause this type of movement.

If the tail is used as a propulsive organ, it is generally flattened, either from side to side, like a fish tail, or top and bottom, like a whale's. In fish the tail is the main driving force; it works on the principle of the screw propeller. The same technique is found among torpedo-shaped aquatic mammals. Here, however, body movements are up and down. The animal's tail flukes are flattened

The bottle-nosed dolphin (above), like all members of the whale group, has a fish-shaped body. It uses its muscular tail and horizontal tail flukes for propulsion. The fin-shaped front limbs are used for steering and balance.

Waterfowl, such as the graylag goose (center), swim with powerful strokes of their webbed feet.

Penguins (bottom) have oarlike flippers instead of wings. They use their hind legs only for steering.

River otters (above) use various body movements and the thrust of a long, muscular tail for swimming.

The ray (right) has wing-shaped pectoral fins. These fins wave gracefully, moving the fish across the sea floor. The tail supplies stability.

On the opposite page: the extinct reptile, a plesiosaur (top), had large rowing limbs; pond turtles (lower left) use their webbed front and hind feet in an alternating paddling rhythm. The otter (lower right) uses its feet for steering and its tail and body for propulsion.

in the horizontal plane, rather than vertically as in fish; that is, the tailfin extends from side to side.

Other aquatic vertebrates displace water by using the principle of the oar and paddle. They move their limbs alternately or together to row the body through water. The adaptive change that has occurred in the anatomy is found in the animal's feet. There has been an evolution from a land foot to a broad, flat surface. This involved either the evolution of webbing between otherwise fairly "regular" toes, or more deep-seated changes in the bone structure of the foot, converting it to a finlike flipper.

The paddlers include ducks, geese, and swans, which use their webbed feet to propel themselves through the water. Birds such as penguins and auks use their flipper-like wings. It is interesting to note that a similar adaptation to aquatic life took place millions of years ago during the Age of Dinosauts. The primitive water bird *Hesperornis* was flightless and had vestigial wings.

Many marine reptiles use rowing techniques to swim. This is particularly true of turtles. Sea turtles use both their front and back flippers for rowing; the latter also serve for balance and ruddering. Fresh-water and pond turtles use their webbed feet very effectively as they chase water insects and small fish. In past ages there were paddle-limbed marine reptiles, the plesiosaurs, who were excellent rowers. They shared the seas with ichthyosaurs. These reptiles, instead of rowing, had evolved a fishlike body and propelling tailfins (as have today's dolphins and whales); their limbs were finlike.

Among mammals, the rowers include the web-footed duckbilled platypus and the flippered seals. Seals and sea lions use their flippers both for land movement and for paddling in the water. However, these mammals propel themselves mainly with sinuous movements of their bodies. Sea lions and fur seals use both front and back flippers in land movement; hair seals, on the other hand, use only their front flippers when they are moving on land.

Beavers have webbed hind feet. They also have a flattened tail. The tail is mainly used for balance; but occasionally it is used as an

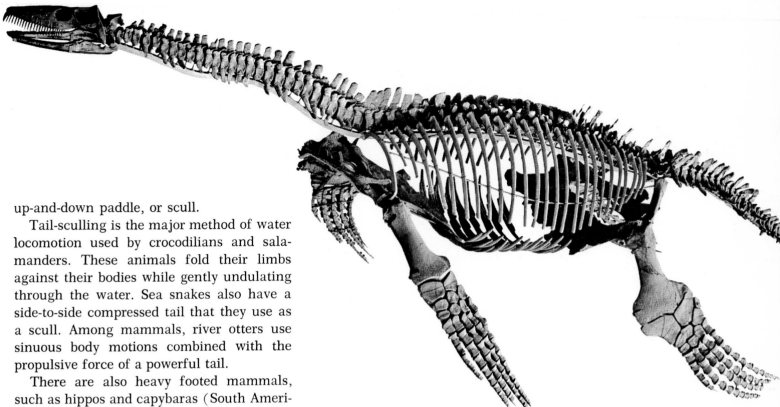

up-and-down paddle, or scull.

Tail-sculling is the major method of water locomotion used by crocodilians and salamanders. These animals fold their limbs against their bodies while gently undulating through the water. Sea snakes also have a side-to-side compressed tail that they use as a scull. Among mammals, river otters use sinuous body motions combined with the propulsive force of a powerful tail.

There are also heavy footed mammals, such as hippos and capybaras (South American rodents), which spend a lot of time in the water. These use a rather clumsy dog paddle when swimming.

Crawling and Walking. When the first amphibian crawled on land, it used finlike structures. Today's amphibians, such as salamanders, have terrestrial limbs instead of fins. Still, they hardly raise their bodies off the ground. Their sprawled-out legs serve as props against the soil; body movement is still in terms of the fish's S-shaped curve. In these amphibians this occurs as a shouldering and hip-thrusting movement that throws one leg forward at a time. This means that the body is always propped up by at least three legs.

The basic sequence of limb movement in a salamander is always the same. It is always at a diagonal across the body. The legs are lifted from the ground (or placed on the ground) in a definite order. If we begin to watch when the right forefoot lifts, the next leg raised is always the left rear. This is followed by the left forelimb, and this in turn by the hind leg on the right side. A crawling baby moves in exactly the same way. In fact, the basic walking pattern of all four-legged vertebrates follows this diagonal sequence.

Most reptiles have the same kind of limbs as amphibians. But many of them can raise their bodies well off the ground—at least for short periods of time.

Among reptiles, snakes present a special

Salamanders (above) use their body muscles for movement on land. They thrust one side of the body forward, then the other. Note the fishlike S-shaped curve of the body. The small legs function mainly as props as the salamander crawls forward.

The monitor (middle) is a lizard. It has the typical sprawled-out legs of a reptile. However, as we see here, it can raise its body well off the ground.

Turtles (bottom) also have legs directed sideways from the body. In spite of this awkward appearance, the pond turtle can move quickly on land.

The Old World water snake (opposite page), like all snakes, moves by curving its body into loops. When it pushes and then straightens the loops against the ground, it moves forward.

84

case. By curving the body into S-shaped loops, contact is made with irregularities of the surface, against which the snakes push. The result is forward movement. Snakes are practically helpless on a completely smooth surface. Some snakes possess big belly scales that can be moved by special muscles that help in locomotion. In a situation such as a narrow tunnel, where a snake cannot loop sideways, it moves forward like an inchworm, shortening and then straightening out its body in what is called the "concertina" movement.

The walk of mammals follows the diagonally sequential limb movement we mentioned earlier. (There are a few exceptions: elephants, giraffes, camels, and hyenas frequently move both legs on the same side in

a gait called pacing. This gives those animals a side-to-side, rolling kind of walk.)

Some mammals have developed specialized movements for rapid locomotion. In a walk, a four-legged animal is always supported by three limbs. Therefore, it can stop in its tracks without falling over. When it speeds up, however, the next limb in the sequence is lifted before the previous one reaches the ground. Thus there is a moment when only two diagonally opposite feet are on the ground. This gait is called a trot; the resulting lack of stability is counterbalanced by the rapid placement of feet.

Only a few mammals are capable of a true gallop. The most noteworthy is the horse. In a gallop only one foot touches the ground at any time; there are even momen-tary periods when all the feet are in midair. In the case of a galloping horse, the muscles that move the limbs impart all the pro-pulsive power; the back muscles play a mi-nor role. This, then, is quite different from the method of fishes, amphibians and rep-tiles, where side-to-side movements of the back are the main source of moving power. However, many mammals do use the power of the back muscles in locomotion. A gallop-ing greyhound, for instance, arches and stretches its body to increase the force and length of its stride. But here the contractions are in the vertical or up-and-down rather than the horizontal or side-to-side plane.

There are quite a few vertebrates that use a bipedal or two-legged walk rather than a four-legged one. The whole class of birds are

The antelope and rhinoc-eroses (opposite page) share the basic mam-malian pattern and posture of four-footed walking. Bears (below), however, often stand upright on their hind legs.

A lesser panda (center, left) walks by placing the whole sole of each foot on the ground.

Birds, such as the In-dian black-necked stork (bottom, left), walk on their toes. Their heels are well off the ground.

Horses (above) are perfectly equipped for rapid movement over dry ground. Their hoofs are actually the tips of what would be the middle toes and fingers in other vertebrates.

A kangaroo (below) balances its weight on a tripod formed by the tail and the long hind legs. During a jump, the tail acts as a counterbalance.

bipedal, since the forefeet are now adapted for flight. Birds have, accordingly, a center of gravity for their bodies that is directly in line with their hind feet rather than toward the middle of the body. Their walking legs, too, are directly beneath the body and they walk with their heels well off the ground.

Walking on the toes is called digitigrade movement. It is also done by many fast moving mammals. The horse, for example, actually stands on the tip of the middle, and only, toe of each foot. These are its hooves; the other toes have disappeared in the course of evolution. Dogs and cats are also digitigrade when they run. The bears, in contrast, are plantigrade. This means that they walk flat-footed, with their heels on the ground.

Man is the only tailless animal that ordinarily walks on two legs. Apes can walk erect, but only for very short periods. Bears, too, can move bipedally on occasion.

A different sort of hind-end balance has been achieved by the long-tailed jumpers. Here the tail is used as a third prop or for counterbalance. Leaping mammals such as kangaroos (marsupials), jerboas, and kangaroo rats (both rodents) propel themselves with power from the long hind legs. During the jump (in which some kangaroos can cover 25 feet) the air-borne tail serves as a counterweight; during hopping, the tail becomes a third prop.

Among reptiles, some lizards, when in a

hurry, can run on their hind legs, using long tails for counterbalance. Many dinosaurs were also bipedal.

The frogs, through evolution, have lost their tails; but they have evolved powerful hind legs that are used for both swimming and jumping. Both frogs and toads hop. Toads can also progress by the more ordinary vertebrate diagonal walking gait.

One does not ordinarily think of fish as walking. However, there are several kinds of fish that have modified fins that they can use for propping themselves against the bottom as they undulate forward.

It is interesting to look at some top speeds of land animals. The cheetah holds the record at 70 m.p.h. Next are some of the gazelles, capable of moving about 60 m.p.h. A running man can hit 20 m.p.h. A man doubles his capacity when mounted on a galloping horse; then he is neck-to-neck with running ostriches, leaping hares, and galloping foxes. Some snakes can actually approach 10 m.p.h. on a short dash. A wild pig can manage 30 m.p.h., which seems to be about average for many animals: the smaller cats, bison, giraffes, moose, bighorn sheep, and even on occasion the cumbersome rhinoceros.

A giraffe can reach a speed of 30 miles per hour. Giraffes use a gait called pacing. This means that the two legs on the same side of the body move at the same time.

Ostriches use enormous strides when in a hurry. They can race along at a speed (about 50 miles per hour) faster than a galloping horse.

Gnus (below), like other antelopes, can move at a 40-miles-per-hour gallop.

Digging and Burrowing.

Digging and Burrowing. It is frequently of advantage to get underground to avoid enemies or temperature extremes on the surface. Also, ants, termites, beetle grubs, earthworms, and plant roots found there can provide nourishment. Domestic dogs frequently dig holes in which to bury bones. Pigs root with their snouts to get at underground plant food.

However, there are representatives from all the classes of vertebrates that are specialized for a fossorial, or burrowing, way of life. Among mammals, moles are probably the best known diggers. Their forelimbs have undergone anatomical changes that make them effective "shovels" in the rapid excavation of long underground mazes in which moles spend their lives. There is a pouched mole in Australia that lives very much the same way. Several rodents also live a mole-like way of life. These full-time burrowers have greatly reduced vision. However, they have very highly developed senses of touch and smell.

Among the part-time burrowers can be numbered many desert rodents (for example, kangaroo rats). These animals spend most

An aardvark (above) looks awkward when it walks. When it digs, however, it is as efficient as a bulldozer.

Mole-rats (right) are rodents that are well-known diggers. Smell is their dominant sense. Their eyes are tiny and they have no outer ears.

Spiny anteaters, or echidnas (far right), are another group of burrowers. They spend their time rooting and digging for ants.

of the day underground. At dusk they come out to gather food.

Many ant- and termite-eaters have sharp digging foreclaws. They use these to open underground nests. The South American ant-eaters share this characteristic with the spiny ant-eater of Australia and New Guinea. The latter lives in burrows that it excavates; when frightened, it literally digs itself into the ground. The African aardvark is another ant- and termite-eating mammal that digs superbly; it spends most of the day in its cool underground den. Many mammals dig out dens in which to live or raise their young. Among these, the badger excels as a subterranean engineer.

Reptiles can count quite a few burrowers among their ranks. Many snakes live underground, at least for part of the time. There are also a number of limbless lizards that have specialized in a fossorial existence. These all use their blunt heads as a digging tool. Desert tortoises dig deep tunnels into the dry ground with shovel-shaped forearms.

Among the amphibians, spade-foot toads are diggers. They are named after a sharp cutting edge on the side of each hind foot that enables them to dig. The peculiar earthworm-shaped caecilians are a whole group of amphibians that live an entirely underground existence.

Certain fish, too, spend a great deal of time buried up to their gills in the sand on the bottom of their watery environment. The slender elongated pipefish, a relative of the seahorses, is one such fish.

The kangaroo rat of the Southwestern American desert spends the day in a cool burrow and only comes out at dusk to feed. It never drinks and can produce water internally from the seeds it eats.

Climbing. Another way to avoid danger on the surface of the ground is to climb into bushes or trees. Also, the arboreal habitat offers many food items such as insect life and plant products (leaves and fruit).

Mostly, arboreal movement is similar to the standard terrestrial walking and running movement. Added to this are grasping devices that prevent falling. Among mammals, grasping hands and feet are particularly characteristic of monkeys, but are also possessed by opossums and certain mice. A prehensile tail—a terminal appendage that can be wrapped around branches—also helps when the animal is high above the ground. South American monkeys, porcupines, arboreal anteaters, and many Australian tree-climbing marsupials have this kind of a device. Tree sloths use sharp, curved claws as grappling hooks with which to move in an upside-down position.

The grasping foot and prehensile tail also figure among reptiles—the Old World chameleon being the best example. Other lizards (e.g. geckos) have specialized toepads. These enable the lizard to hang on to almost completely smooth surfaces, as it chases insects up and down rocks or walls.

A suction-disc kind of toe is a characteristic of tree frogs. Suction pads are also found on the hands and feet of certain primitive primates, the tarsiers—an example of how similar adaptive solutions to a problem frequently evolve independently among different animals.

The tarsier (opposite page) is a hopper on the branches of trees. Its fingers and toes have suction-cup tips, which help it hold onto the tree.

A pangolin (top) inches its way up a tree trunk. Heavy claws serve as grappling hooks.

The Old World chameleon (center) has two obvious features keyed to climbing: its "wrap-around" tail and its pincherlike toes.

The tree frog (bottom, far left) is quite similar to the tarsier in its climbing adaptations.

The flying squirrel, (bottom, center) is not really a flier; it glides. A membrane of skin stretched between front and hind limbs acts as a parachute.

The koala (below), an Australian marsupial, has fingers and toes arranged very much like those of a chameleon.

This trained falcon has been carried aloft by the power of its beating wings. Now it can soar effortlessly in search of prey. Note the spread feathers along the wing tips and the fanned-out tail.

Gliding. Any anatomical change that increases an animal's spread-out surface—on the principal of a parachute—is an advantage in maneuvering. Quite a few vertebrates are able to glide. Many arboreal vertebrates, for example, leap from branch to branch. In this process, they are in free fall part of the time.

Among mammals, the best gliders are flying squirrels, flying phalangers (a kind of Australian marsupial), and the so-called "flying lemurs," or colugos. All these have a membrane of skin extending from the sides of the body and attached to the hind and front limbs. With legs spread and often with fluffy tails acting as controls, these mammals can glide considerable distances between trees and branches or to the ground.

Some lizards also have gliding membranes. These can be extended like wings by way of elongated ribs along the sides of the body. Certain tree snakes can flatten their bodies to act as parachutes during glides. Even the frogs have gliders in their ranks—certain Asiatic tree frogs that extend the webbing between their long hind toes.

True Flight. The ability to fly is quite different from the ability to glide passively. Few vertebrates are able to fly. However, one whole class of vertebrates, the birds, is distinguished by its ability to stay aloft through the active beating of wings displacing air.

The earliest flying vertebrates were reptiles called pterosaurs. These animals lived millions of years ago. Pterosaurs had a thin membrane extending from the top of a greatly elongated fourth finger to the hind legs. They were probably passive gliders rather than true fliers. There were many kinds of pterosaurs. Some were no bigger than sparrows. Others had 25-foot wing-

The extinct "flying" reptile (below) is a large pterosaur. It lived about 150 million years ago. Pterosaurs were mostly gliders.

The screech owl (bottom left) nicely demonstrates the down-stroke wing position during the flapping cycle. Note how the wing tips almost meet in front of the head.

This booby (above) spends its time over the water, only returning to land to breed. It propels itself by alternate flapping and long glides.

95

spreads. But all became extinct about the time that the first birds appeared on earth.

Birds, of course, also use simple gliding techniques during flight. Some, like shearwaters and albatrosses, can glide low over the water for miles with barely a wingbeat. And eagles and vultures can soar for long distances at great heights.

When a bird beats its wings downward, it provides a lifting force that is equal to the weight of its body, and a forward thrust equal to the backward drag of the air.

We can compare a bird with a helicopter. A bird's flapping wings are the equivalent of a helicopter's rotor and screw-blade. Control during flight is achieved by using the tail feathers as a horizontal rudder, and partly by changing the shape and posture of the wings. The main propulsion during active flight seems to be the downward stroke of the wing. This is brought about by the heavy muscles attached to the bird's keeled breastbone.

The down stroke begins with the wings fully extended, stretched up over the back of the bird. Both wings then stroke downward and forward to meet in front of the body. The backward and upward stroke now follows. It first uncovers the head of the bird, and then draws the wing back and up in position for a new downward stroke.

Besides birds, only the bats have mastered true flight. They utilize a membrane of skin stretched between three or four fingers, the sides of the body and the hind legs.

The powerful hawk (opposite page) is braking with its outstretched wings and tail. Its talons are extended as it comes in for the kill. Despite the snake's desperate dash, it doesn't have a chance against the hawk.

Like all bats, the pipistrelle (below) flies like a bird. Its wings, however, are not feathered. They are membranes of skin that extend between several fingers, the sides of the body, and the hind legs.

The tuatara of New Zealand (right) blends in well with its background. But this has not been enough to protect it from man. It survives now on only a few rocky islets.

The green and tan splotches on the skin of this toad (below) make it almost invisible on the forest floor.

Protection

An animal may be extraordinarily successful at feeding, reproducing, and movement. But this means little if the animal is vulnerable to attack. Unless an animal can defend itself against enemies, it will not survive for long.

All animals have evolved means of protection that enable them to survive in their environments. Sometimes the defense is passive and individual. Sometimes it involves the cooperation of a large group. For some, the best defense is offense. In each case, wariness is of utmost importance. Every animal must be aware of ever-present danger from enemies if he is not to be a "goner."

In those groups in which great self-confidence made its members lose track of this important rule, results have been disastrous. Great cats, like the tigers, seemed invulnerable to enemies because of their great strength. But they have been hunted almost to extinction by man, the most thoughtless killer ever to have walked the earth. The same is true for such groups as elephants, eagles, rhinoceroses, and bison. In contrast, smaller animals have always had to be alert to danger. Thus they have been more successful in maintaining their place in this man-dominated environment.

Remember that, in the total history of nature, man's stay on earth is of very recent origin. Some animals, whose survival has been threatened by man, are beginning to adapt to his presence. Coyotes, for instance, manage to survive even though there has long been a campaign to eradicate them. They have even extended their range and now occupy territories they had not inhabited in the past.

The leopard's camouflage is mainly offensive rather than defensive. With his spotted coat, he blends into the background; his victims are unaware of his presence until too late.

Camouflage and Warning Signals. All the various means of defense used by animals have been copied by mankind for use against one another. One of the most popular has been camouflage. In the animal kingdom camouflage may be used passively, as in birds, in order to hide from one's enemies. Camouflage may be used aggressively, as in leopards; they wait in ambush until exactly the right moment for the kill. Some animals combine both motives; lizards, for instance, hide from enemies while waiting inconspicuously for insects.

Camouflage usually has to do with color. Protective coloration involves blending in so perfectly with one's surroundings that one cannot be seen. Some lizards have a remarkable ability to change their color to correspond with the immediate surroundings. Old World chameleons are the absolute masters of camouflage. Their skin contains star-shaped color cells of black, yellow, red, and white. These cells contain grains of pigment that contract and expand in response to stimulation from the nerves. As one color expands, another contracts. This enables a chameleon to change quickly from black to red, for instance, as the occasion demands. If both red and yellow expand simultaneously, the resulting coloration will be orange.

Most animals have just one pattern of coloration, tied to one environmental situation. They will, therefore, spend the majority of their time in that situation. Here they will feel protected. They will venture into other surroundings only at times of minimum danger. Young deer, for instance, are spotted to blend with the sun-dappled forest in which they spend their days. Only during the evening, when visibility is lessened, will they go into the meadows to feed.

Each class of animals has members that rely on camouflage for protection. There are fish living near the bottom of the sea that blend with the coral or the sand. Freshwater bottom-dwellers look like rocks. There are frogs and toads that are dappled to blend with the moist, swamp areas they inhabit; salamanders that look like rocks or earth; snakes like grass or leaves. Bob whites are colored to be inconspicuous in high grass, and weasels are earth-colored in the summer and snow-colored in the winter.

The best defense of some animals is in looking dangerous. These animals do not blend with their surroundings. Rather, they stand out starkly against them. Some of these animals are poisonous and the rest of the animal world has learned to associate brilliant colors with danger. Very few animals will closely approach the brightly-colored coral snake. This benefits several quite harmless creatures that have bright yellow or red coloring; though harmless, their coloring frightens off potential enemies. Similarly, few animals ignore the striking black-and-white fur of a skunk.

Another method of camouflage is the use of unusual or startling shapes. There are, for instance, chameleons that look like dried leaves. Certain geckos resemble bark. Many lizards have frills or collars that they can extend to appear ferocious. Even frogs have throat pouches that they can blow out to seem bigger. Some snakes have tails that are shaped like heads; these confuse their enemies into attacking the wrong end.

The green mamba (left) has two very effective defenses. Its coloring blends with its green environment. Also, it has an extremely deadly poison.

Larks (center) nest on the ground. Their protective coloring is very important to their survival.

Fish (bottom) frequently blend with their surroundings. This fish can scarcely be distinguished from the rocks.

Members of the rockfish, or scorpion fish, group have fin spines to protect themselves. One rockfish, the turkey fish (below), has venom glands attached to the spines, making them even more effective.

Armor and Spines. Another effective method of protection is the use of heavy plating to protect the vulnerable parts of the body.

A turtle is like a walking tank. It plods slowly along, well protected by its hard shell. Its back and underside are completely covered with a shield of fused, bony plates. In an emergency, the turtle can withdraw its head, arm, legs, and tail through openings in the shell. This arrangement is complex and unique to turtles. The anatomical adaptations that have made this defense possible are indeed wondrous. The ribs of the turtle have grown outward; they cover the bony girdles to which the limbs attach and support the top shell, or carapace. The

bottom shell, or plastron, connects to the carapace along the sides. The entire shell is covered with hornlike plates.

The armor of the armadillo is different, but just as effective. Over the shoulders and hips there are solid bony shields. Between these shields are movable bands of armor that offer flexibility as well as protection. There is also armor on the head and tail. If danger seems imminent, the flexibility of his back allows one kind of armadillo to roll into a tight ball. In this position his vulnerable underparts are completely hidden.

Some animals have sharp spines that protect them. Burrfish are also called "balloon-fish" and "porcupine fish." All three names are apt. These creatures have hollow spines that normally lie against the body. When threatened, the fish inflate themselves into veritable balloons of air; then the spines stand out straight.

Porcupines, too, have long quills for use against intruders. Normally peace-loving, these rodents are quite able to care for themselves in an emergency. They simply turn their backs, raise and vibrate their quills, and wait. If the threat is not immediately removed, the porcupine runs backward and spears the interloper unmercifully.

The Mediterranean land tortoise (top) and the armadillo of America (bottom) are covered with shields of bony plates. The tortoise's shell is a solid shield. The shell has openings for the head and legs, into which the tortoise withdraws for protection. The armadillo's shell consists of solid shields over shoulders and hips, with movable bands of shell between.

The Old World porcupine (center) is covered with quills. When threatened, this rodent raises its quills, turns its back on the intruder, and stands ready to defend itself.

Poison. There are several types of animals whose mastery in the use of poison makes the Borgias look like sissies. Animals, however, unlike humans, use this substance only for self-defense or to help in acquiring food. Indeed, many animals that need their poison-killing facility to keep them supplied with food, hesitate to use it for protection and give ample warning to approaching intruders.

Scorpion fish, however, use their poison only for protection. These odd-looking creatures hover on the bottom of shallow seas. They have strong, elongated spines located around the head and fins. Beneath each spine is a poison gland; a hollow groove runs from the gland to the tip of the spine. Any pressure against the tip causes the gland to eject its venom into the puncture made by the spine. The poisonous jab of some species can kill a human being. That of other species may paralyze. The least that can be expected is intense pain.

Stingrays are almost as ominous as they look. Their undulating, wide-winged pectoral fins allow them to skim with seeming effortlessness across the bottom of the sea. From the top surface of the whiplike tail, about three-quarters of the way down, project one or two flattened spines.

Beneath the spine are venom glands. When the stingray is aroused, it whips its flexible spine-bearing tail about in several directions. It strikes with astonishing force any organism it considers a foe. As stingrays count on their swimming ability and sharp teeth to procure the food they need, the terrifying tail is used solely for protection.

Many amphibians have a little poison in their skins. In most, it is barely enough to discourage the small mammals that usually prey upon them. One group, however, is known as the "arrow poison" frogs; South American Indians have found the venom secreted by these amphibians to be fatally effective in hunting small game.

No poison is as highly feared as that possessed by the venomous snakes. Engendering this fear is the threatening posture of the snake or the warning sound it makes. Snakes, however, need their poison to get food and are loathe to waste it in defense. It takes severe provocation to make a snake strike. Rattlesnakes and adders have poison that attacks the blood system of their victims. The poison of cobras affects the nervous system. In all cases, the poison is located in modified salivary glands, and is ejected through canals within the fangs.

The only poisonous lizards are the gila monster and beaded lizard. Their poison mechanism is less efficient than that of snakes. They have no way of directly injecting the venom. It simply runs along grooves at the front of the teeth from glands located in the jaws.

The egg-laying platypus seems to have few natural enemies. But males have spurs on their ankles connected by narrow canals to poison glands. The venom from these glands is used in defense and is powerful enough to incapacitate a man.

Some species of cobra, like the ringhals (above), spit, or spray, their deadly venom at an enemy. They can spray the venom a distance of seven feet or more.

The Gila monster (left) is a venomous lizard. Unlike most lizards, Gila monsters move very slowly. Their venom apparatus is less efficient than that of the snakes.

Herding and Getting Away Fast.

The idea of safety in numbers is not unique to humans. Many groups of animals operate on the same premise. In some, the herding technique has been refined to a fine art.

Schools of fish are a familiar sight, even in acquariums, in certain species. There are, in fact, 4,000 species that practice schooling as a daily part of their lives. Schools of fish line up with exact distances between each fish. It is as though an army sergeant were parading his troops—they move and turn with such extraordinary precision. But, oddly enough, there are no leaders at the front; the direction seems to come from the middle of the school. Among other advantages, the precision of movement makes the school appear to be one, very large organism.

Ostriches are gregarious birds. Not only do they live in small groups of their own kinds, but frequently they join other plains animals such as antelopes and zebras. The association is mutually advantageous. The mammals flush live food (reptiles and insects) that ostriches enjoy, while the seven-foot-tall birds stand guard.

Although ostriches do not fly, they have no trouble escaping from danger. Some members of the group are always on guard. With their seven-foot height and sharp eyesight, they can spot enemies quickly. When alarmed, the running speed of ostriches is equal to or better than that of most enemies.

Pelicans (above) live
communally and fly in
formation, beating their
wings together. When
the leader spreads
his wings to glide, the
whole group follows.

For a deer (left), protection is mainly a matter
of escape. Most deer are
capable of great speed
when danger threatens
them.

Marabou storks (right) are gathered together to dine. They have many of the habits and behavior of vultures, and feed mainly on carrion.

The birds pictured below left are called "painted storks," but they are actually ibises. They are very social and during nesting form groups that may number in the thousands. When in flight, they engage in group gliding.

A school of Atlantic mackerel (center right) will migrate together from Maine to Chesapeake Bay and back again.

Shore birds like those at bottom right usually feed together on sea food and nest along the beaches in colonies.

Several methods of dealing with the enemy have been worked out by animals that live in herds. In some, the most vigilant members of the group sound the alert and everyone takes to his heels. In others, a defensive position is formed. Musk oxen live in herds numbering up to 100. When they are threatened by the wolves that prey upon them, they form a tight circle with the calves inside. Thus the enemy is presented with a unified rank of ominous horns. This is enough to discourage wolves. Unfortunately, it does not work well against men with guns, and many herds have been completely killed off by sportsmen.

Other mammals that herd depend on speed to escape. In giraffe herds, for example, it is the females that keep watch. With their very keen sense of hearing, they are quick to sense danger and give the alarm. The group then immediately takes off with surprising speed for such ungainly looking animals.

Herd animals are not the only ones that depend on speed for safety. Any animal without the benefit of protective coloring, poison or armor finds that its best means of defense is escape. This applies to animals in the sea, in the air, and on land. It applies to both communal and solitary animals.

Small fish swim rapidly away from big fish. Frogs and rabbits have long hind legs to carry them in long jumps away from pursuers. In Australia, kangaroos use their powerful legs to hop away from wild dogs and marsupial carnivores. Ducks, when endangered on land, take quickly to the air. Desert lizards scurry quickly through the sand. Squirrels scamper wildly through the trees when threatened, as do the monkeys. In each of these groups, the fastest animal is the one most likely to survive.

Part of a giraffe herd has come for a drink of water. Giraffes travel in herds of about 6 to 15 individuals. Each herd consists of an adult male, several females with their calves, and a few adolescent males. The females keep watch and give alarm if danger seems near.

The lamprey (right) is a survivor of an early group of vertebrates, the jawless fish. Note the holes along the side, behind the eye. These are the openings of the gill pouches. These primitive fish do not have upper and lower jaws. They attach themselves as parasites to other fish.

These small sharks (center) are smooth dogfish from the Mediterranean. They prey on other fish and also eat invertebrates such as marine worms.

The shark (below) is a tiger, or leopard, shark. Note the triangular fin along its back and the paired fins on its underside. The tiger shark hunts fish and marine mammals. It is also a scavenger on the ocean's bottom.

The thornback ray (opposite page) shows the waving movement of its expanded fins. Its skeleton is made of cartilage rather than bone.

Classification

To understand the world of animals, some method of classifying, of finding relationships, is absolutely necessary. Zoologists have devised a system that classifies animals according to their physical characteristics.

Within the vertebrates, there are seven major subdivisions called classes. Three of these are commonly called fishes: the jawless fishes, the cartilaginous fishes, and the bony fishes. The other four are the amphibians, reptiles, birds, and mammals. Each class can be broken down further, for some animals bear more obvious relationships to each other than to others of the same class. Therefore, classes are divided into orders, and within each order there are families. Families are broken down still further into genera, and genera into species.

Fishes

Although all the animals we know as fishes bear certain similarities to each other, there are such sharp distinctions among these forms that they are usually considered separately. Hagfishes and lampreys form one

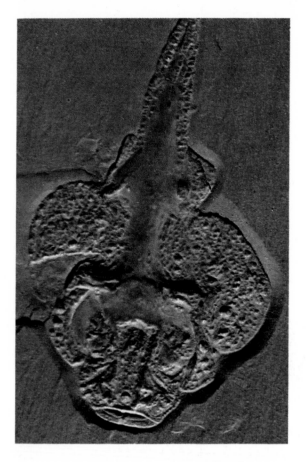

The fossil fish at right resembles the living skates and rays. It is actually a 400-million-year-old member of an ancient group of fish with jaws. Their relationship to later fish is not clear. The internal skeleton of the fossil was bony, not cartilaginous.

The ray-finned bony fishes, or teleosts, include many diverse subgroups or orders. The brook trout (bottom left) is a typical fish. So are the two snakelike eels (bottom right).

group, sharks and rays another, and all the bony fishes form the third.

Fishes are the most ancient class of vertebrates. Their history began more than 400 million years ago. In the seas of that eerie, silent period, there lived a multitude of invertebrates. Some invertebrates slowly evolved characteristics leading to the vertebrate body. As time passed, the vertebrates evolved from fish to amphibian to reptile to bird and mammal, culminating in that most dominant of mammals, man. But one group of vertebrates remained in the oceans to remind us of our humble origin.

Lampreys. Humiliating as it may be, the ancestor of all vertebrate life was a creature quite similar to the modern lamprey. Lampreys are naked, eel-like creatures without jaws. In their youth, they live on the bottoms of streams and suck up small animals with disclike, toothless mouths. As they mature and grow teeth, they become parasites, attaching themselves to passing fish; they bore a hole and suck the body juices.

The Australian lungfish is one of three kinds of surviving lungfish. They first appeared at a time when several groups of lobe-finned fish were common in fresh water. Lungfish were never on a direct ancestral line to amphibians. Their fins, however, resemble those of the lobe-fins that did move onto land.

A lamprey has a single nostril on top of its head, with eyes on either side. The powerful sucker is lined with horny "teeth," which surround the mouth. On the head behind the nose lies a third eye known as the pineal eye.

The first vertebrates did not go through a parasitic stage. Rather, they remained vacuum-cleaner-type feeders, sucking in small animal life in their path. They were jawless and did not have pectoral fins. The primitive vertebral column had not yet evolved into a strong, well-articulated structure. Many types of jawless fishes evolved, including some with heavy armor and head shields.

A major step in vertebrate evolution took place with the development of the first jawed fishes. An animal equipped with jaws has a much greater range of feeding possibilities than a jawless animal. Two pairs of fins, so necessary to expert swimming, also developed.

Armed with well-articulated vertebral columns, snapping jaws, and well-situated fins, fishes began to populate the seas. Today, more than 20,000 species are scattered throughout the world.

Sharks and rays are divided from the bulk of the species because of their skeleton, which is composed of cartilage rather than bone. Both groups, sharks and bony fishes, arose from primitive jawed fishes at about the same point in history. However, sharks and rays perfected their evolution at a very early point, remaining virtually unchanged for millions of years. The bony fishes went on to evolve into thousands of types, adapted to every kind of watery environment.

Sharks and Rays. Modern sharks and rays are mainly marine creatures. They can be found in all the seas of the world. Although some reach a length of 40 feet, most species are smaller; some never attain to more than two feet. All sharks and rays are carnivorous.

Sharks are rather terrifying creatures. One justifiable reason for fearing them is the rows of daggerlike teeth. These teeth are constantly renewed, the worn out ones being replaced by new ones. Within the skin of a shark are other tiny "teeth," sharp, closely set pieces of bone that are very abrasive.

Rays are equally ominous in appearance, with their flat, winglike fins extended as they skim silently by. Actually, of all the rays, only the stingray is dangerous to man.

Bony Fishes. One order of modern bony fishes, that to which the sturgeon belongs, is quite archaic. At one time, fish like these dominated in the seas. Sturgeons have small mouths and weak jaws that can be swung downward and forward when they feed. The upper lobe of the tail is somewhat longer than the lower. Although their ancestors had bony skeletons, sturgeons are more cartilaginous than other bony fish and have fewer scales.

The sturgeonlike fish gave rise to a group of fish more like the modern garpike. These thick-scaled fish have shorter, deeper bodies and a tail that is almost symmetrical.

From these early groups evolved fish that had even shorter, more symmetrical tails. The scales were thinned down more and there were advances in the structure of the skull, particularly the jaw mechanism. This line of fish evolution gave rise to most of the modern bony fishes.

Salmon, herrings, and trout are some of the most primitive members of this modern group. They have soft rays in their fins, an open duct to the air bladder, and pelvic fins that are placed far back on the body.

Carp and goldfish are somewhat more advanced. Their specialization consists of having the front vertebrae form a chain of bones that connects the air bladder to the inner ear.

Eels broke away early from this main line of evolution. They have no pelvic fins; their back and belly fins are usually combined with the tail fin. Most eels lack scales.

Pike and sticklefish are intermediate between the carp and the most advanced fishes. There is an advance in the structure of the shoulder girdle, and the air bladder has an opening that is continuous with the gut. The fins have soft rays.

The most highly developed fishes have belly fins and stiff rays at the front of the back. The duct of the air bladder is closed, the body shortened, and the pelvic fins are situated far forward. The peak of this evolutionary line can be seen in the modern perch.

While most of the bony fishes were evolving in the manner described above, one line remained quite distinct. This line had no rays in the fins. Instead, it had fleshy lobes. The coelacanth, from deep in the oceans around southeastern Africa, is a living reminder of ancient days. Although not very successful as fishes, the lobe-fins are very important to vertebrate history. It was a lobe-fin that took the first step from sea to land and ultimately led to the first amphibian.

A moray eel (opposite page) lunges from his hiding place in the reef. Morays are powerful and dreaded ocean hunters.

Flounders and soles (center) can change color to match their resting surface. When the fish mature, they stay close to the ocean bottom. The same side of the fish always stays on top, and the eye on the underside moves across to join the other eye on top.

This bottom-dwelling weaverfish (below, left) has poison spines along the back and on the cheek region. These fishes stay near the bottom and frequently bury themselves under the sand.

Coral fish such as the butterfly fish (bottom right) are often very brilliantly colored. This appears to be a way of signaling territory limits to others of their species.

Amphibians

Amphibians were the first vertebrates to adapt to land. For a while, they were the only vertebrates on land. There were invertebrates, such as spiders, but these satisfied hunger and offered no competition. During those early days, the amphibians developed in many different ways, and a great variety of forms appeared.

One of the oldest lines of amphibians is known as the labyrinthodonts. It is within this group that the characteristics typical of amphibians developed. Some of these early types clung pretty much to the water; others developed into active land-dwellers, sometimes reaching a length of six feet. Some were heavily armored; others had strange body proportions with huge, flat heads and tiny feet. Another type, the lepospondyls, never became very large and lived mostly in swampy areas. Some of them were legless with snakelike bodies. Others had wide, triangular heads.

From all these early amphibians, each developing in its own way, there evolved only three orders that are still in existence today. Those of labyrinthodont descent are the anurans, or salientians. These very successful animals are better known as frogs and toads. Today there are frog species on every continent except Antarctica. Toads are absent in Australia and the Antarctic. Toads are not as quick as frogs. However, toads have an additional protection to compensate for their lack of speed. This is a bitter substance exuded from skin glands; it discourages a predator from taking a toad into its mouth. Frogs and toads are not equipped to live in deserts. But they are remarkably

Old World newts, like the one below, live on land for most of the year. However, during the breeding season they live in the water. The male then has a frilled red crest on his back.

adept at finding moisture in semi-arid situations. Nor do they live near the sea; salt water is fatal to them. They can withstand extremes in temperature; thus there are frogs and toads in the Yukon as well as in equatorial forests.

There are 2600 species of anurans. In spite of their differences, they have common characteristics that clearly separate them from other amphibians. They are the only tailless amphibians and their long hind legs are quite distinct. Frogs and toads have no neck. As a consequence, they cannot turn their heads easily. Anurans use their hind legs in swimming. In contrast, salamanders rely on their tails for propulsion.

Although many individual salamanders may be seen in a favorable environment at a given moment, there are far fewer species in this order than in the anurans. Salamanders and newts, known as the caudates, number just 280 species. Like toads and frogs, caudates live in moist areas throughout the world. There are, however, no caudates in South America or Australia, nor are they found in most parts of Africa.

Many species of salamanders spend their adult lives on land in moist underbrush. A few actually live in trees. Others live an aquatic existence; some of these, found in deep, cold waters, never make the transformation from larva to adult. They do reach sexual maturity, enabling them to breed; but they retain their gills and other larval characteristics. Other salamanders spend their lives in moist caves. In these places of eternal darkness sight is an unnecessary sense; cave salamanders are blind.

Each caudate species has its own courtship pattern. The female of one species will

The California slender salamander (center) has tiny legs unsuited to walking. It moves like a snake. This salamander likes to live in burrows but cannot dig one itself. Thus it "borrows" those of other animals.

Fire salamanders (bottom left) mate on land in July. In the following May, the female enters the water to give birth to live young. From 10 to 50 one-inch-long young are born. Each has well-developed arms and legs. When adult these fire salamander larvae will live entirely on land.

Central American caecelians (bottom right) are burrowing amphibians without limbs. Their eyes are small and weak. However, they have a tentacle on their head that acts as a sense organ.

not respond to the ritual advances of a male of any other species, thus keeping each group distinct.

The general shape of the salamander's body, coupled with the shortness of its legs and the length of its tail, makes locomotion different from that of the anurans. Caudates are creepers rather than jumpers. However when alarmed, many species do leap.

The wormlike caecilians are mysterious amphibians. Living in burrows beneath the ground, the caecilian's pattern of life is a private affair, almost unknown to man.

Although at a casual glance the caecilians look like earthworms, they can easily be distinguished by the presence of a mouth and eyes. Actually, the eyes are useless. Caecilians are quite blind and "see" by means of small touch-sensitive tentacles that lie between the eyes and the mouth. They have no legs, the head is blunt and the tail short.

Caecilians belong to the third order of amphibians, the Apoda, of which there are 100 species. Most of these live in Central and South America. Others can be found in the warm parts of Africa and Asia.

The eastern spadefoot toad (right) lives in sandy lowlands of the eastern United States. It has a crescent-shaped structure on each hind foot. This forms a shovel for digging out burrows. During mating season the males sing in chorus. The sound they make is something like the cawing of a crow.

The golden mantella of Madagascar (opposite page, top) is quite different from other frogs in its family, the Ranidae. Unlike them it has short legs and a small, broad body.

The European natterjack toad (opposite page, bottom) has such short legs that he cannot hop. Instead, natterjacks run almost as quickly as a mouse.

The skin of a caecilian is different from that of other amphibians. Though it feels slimy on the outside, beneath the surface there are small scales.

Caecilians can grow to be as long as four feet, but they are never very wide. The largest diameter known is only one inch. Some females do give live birth and these, of course, become quite stout temporarily. Caecilians probably live on a diet of earthworms and termites, although no one is really sure. They themselves are considered delectable by several species of snakes.

Reptiles

Some of the labyrinthodont amphibians became frogs and toads. Others took a very different evolutionary route—one that led to the reptiles. The big innovation in these early reptiles was the development of the amniote egg. This egg is fertilized inside the female's body by the male. Sometimes it is laid in a depression in the ground; less frequently it is carried within the mother until hatching time. In either case, it frees the animal of the necessity to return to water to breed.

Thus, the reptiles were able to inhabit more of the surface of the land and exploit many of the situations unavailable to the moisture-clinging amphibians. The amniote egg consists of a sac holding the embryo suspended in a pool of liquid, another sac that contains waste products given off by the embryo, and a huge quantity of yolk from which the embryo feeds. It is surrounded by a thick, leathery shell. The shell protects the egg; pores in the shell allow oxygen to pass in and carbon dioxide out.

Once this egg evolved, the reptiles branched out greatly. Eventually, they became the ruling animals of the world. There were medium to enormous reptiles on land—those we call dinosaurs. Some developed leathery wings and took to the skies. Others, oddly enough, after having won the battle for land supremacy, reverted to a watery environment.

For millions of years, the reptiles held sway. Their success was overwhelming. Then environmental conditions changed. One by one, the impressive ruling reptiles died out, leaving just the small to medium-sized reptiles we know today.

The 250-million-year-old fossil below is that of Seymouria. *It is one of the linking forms between amphibians and reptiles. The skeleton has many features like those of amphibians and many others like the reptiles. Zoologists cannot agree to which of the two classes* Seymouria *belongs. In any case the large head, broad body, and sprawled out legs give us an idea of how the earliest reptiles looked.*

Turtles (opposite page) are highly specialized, though basically very primitive reptiles. They are specialized because of their protective shell and horny, beaked jaws. Other features such as their skull and legs, are like those of early reptiles called cotylosaurs.

The four living orders are: The Testudinata (turtles), the Crocodilia (crocodiles), the Rhynchocephalia (tuatara), and the Squamata (lizards and snakes). The tuatara lives only in New Zealand and probably has been fairly restricted throughout its history. The crocodilians have done very well in the tropical areas of the world. Snakes, lizards, and turtles have thrived in many varied locations. Although no longer dominant, the reptiles of today are a very successful class.

The first turtles made their appearance during the Age of Dinosaurs. They have remained relatively unchanged since that time. The heavy shell that characterizes this order was already present in those ancient days; but turtles may not have been able to pull in their heads and legs for the complete protection most of them now enjoy.

There are about 200 species of turtles. Some are called tortoises and occasionally terrapins. Some varieties live out most of their lives on land. Others are more aquatic, preferring the calm of a small pond. There are species that inhabit the seas of the world and species that live in burrows in the desert sands.

In general, turtles that live on land have sturdy columnar legs; these support the bulk of the shell in moving across hard ground. Marine turtles have less shell for extra buoyancy. Generally, they are larger than the land species. The legs of sea turtles are flipperlike to aid in swimming while pond turtles have webbed feet. Turtles range in size from about 12 inches to almost 6 feet. The largest of them weighs upward of 1,000 pounds. They live in all the temperate regions of the world, including Australia.

Land turtles live on a varied diet with an emphasis on vegetation. Water turtles are more carnivorous, feeding on fish, worms and other vertebrates. Sea turtles are vegetarians.

Crocodilians inhabit only the tropics and subtropics. The large, aggressive crocodilians are the closest surviving relatives of the dinosaurs. In many respects they are the most advanced of reptiles. They have, for instance, a heart that is four-chambered,

The Nile crocodile (below) is a typical crocodilian. This group also includes alligators and long-snouted gavials. Crocodilians are the only surviving archosaurs (or ruling reptiles). The others are the extinct dinosaurs and gliding reptiles. Zoologists frequently turn to the crocodile when they try to imagine what the soft parts and behavior of dinosaurs were like.

socketed teeth, and a palate that separates the mouth from the nasal canals. The first known crocodile was rather small; its hind legs were larger than the forelimbs, indicating its descent from a two-legged ancestor. Other types appeared, some of which became marine animals with paddlelike legs and a tail-fin.

Today's crocodilians of the order Crocodilia number 23 species. These are divided into three families: the gavials, the alligators, and the crocodiles. They all look quite similar, but can be distinguished by their snouts: that of the gavial is long and slender; the alligator's is blunt and short; and the crocodile's lies somewhere in-between.

All crocodilians have a protective covering of bony plates inside the skin across the back. But these plates are not fused, so the crocodilians are capable of great flexibility and speed. They have partly webbed feet. The eyes, nostrils, and ears are placed high on the head. This allows crocodilians to be almost completely submerged without loss of their senses. They have large, strong jaws,

The tuatara from New Zealand (top) is the only living species of a whole order of reptiles, the rhynchocephalians. The tuatara has a "third" eye on top of its head. This is not too unusual. Many extinct lower vertebrates and several living lizards have this structure. These third eyes do not form clear visual images. Instead they seem to be sensitive just to light and heat.

The four-foot-long skull (center) is from one of the largest flesh-eating dinosaurs, Tyrannosaurus rex. It has six-inch teeth, each of which is notched along the edges for better slicing action.

The three-foot-long East Indian water lizard (bottom) lives among forests and streams. As the lizard swims, he moves his sailfin tail from side to side. This motion helps push him through the water.

and very sharp teeth, enabling them to hunt and eat fish and meat with efficiency.

Lizards and snakes belong to the order Squamata. They form the largest and most diverse group of living reptiles. There are about 5,700 species. The squamates have enjoyed this great diversity almost since the end of the Age of Dinosaurs. Early species were quite lizardlike; indeed, many modern lizards retain primitive characteristics such as unsocketed teeth. The snakes are the youngest of all the reptiles, although their line goes back millions of years. Their adaptations—leglessness, elongation of the body, and widely opening jaws—have stood them in good stead since their beginnings. Be-

cause snakes are low to the ground, they can hide easily in debris or under rocks.

Lizards range in size from a few inches to ten feet in length. There are running, climbing, gliding, and burrowing forms. Some lizards are legless like snakes, but they have movable eyelids and their lower jaws are different. Lizards inhabit most of the warm and temperate areas of the world.

Snakes are probably descended from burrowing lizards. Unlike lizards, snakes do not possess movable eyelids. They have clear eyelids that are fused together, giving them an odd, fixed stare. But the main difference is the lack of fusion between the two parts of the lower jaw. This permits widening so that

the snake can swallow objects larger than its own diameter.

Snakes live on the ground, in trees, in burrows, and in the water. There are even marine snakes in the oceans of the world. Most snakes live in the tropics, but there are species in the colder parts of the world. Indeed, one type has even been found within the Arctic Circle. Areas with no snakes at all are Iceland and New Zealand.

The tuatara is the only surviving member of the ancient order Rhynchocephalia. The single species is found only on a few islands off New Zealand. At first glance tuataras look like large lizards, but their skull is differently constructed and more primitive.

The cobra's dangerous reputation (left) is well-founded. Its nerve poison is quite deadly. It is injected from two fangs, one in each side of the upper jaw. This cobra is in the warning posture, with its head raised and its hood widely expanded.

The saw-scaled viper (lower left) may be the most dangerous of all poisonous snakes. This is because of the extreme potency of its poison. The viper lives in deserts and semi-deserts from North Africa to India. When annoyed, it rubs its scales together, making a warning hissing sound.

Turkeys are strictly New World birds. The ocellated turkey (upper left) is found in Yucatan, Guatemala, and British Honduras. It lives in bushy lowlands that are partially forested.

The kiwi (upper right) is an unusual bird of New Zealand. Unlike other birds, which depend largely on sight, kiwis rely on their fine sense of smell. They have no external wings and no tail feathers. Kiwis live in dense forests in burrows. They sleep by day and come out at night to hunt.

Egrets (right) belong to the heron family. They have slim bodies, long, thin bills, and beautiful plumage. Most egrets feed and nest together in large groups.

Birds

During the Age of Dinosaurs, some reptiles began to adapt to flight. Some of them retained their reptilian characteristics but added membranes of skin attached to one long finger and the sides of the body to serve as wings. Others developed feathers and, ultimately, other birdlike characteristics. The first of these, the pterosaurs, became extinct along with the dinosaurs. The latter, the birds, have been remarkably successful since their advent.

Archaeopteryx was one of the first birds. It had a reptilian skull, a long neck and a long bony tail. But there were feathers, and the jaws which probably housed teeth were, nevertheless, beak-shaped. Also, *Archaeopteryx* had a large brain case, indicating the sort of complex nervous system needed by a flying vertebrate.

In time, birds became less reptilian and typical bird characteristics appeared. The bones of the hand were fused, the pelvis became firmly anchored to the back, and the bony tail was reduced. The breastbone became enlarged for the attachment of wing muscles.

Modern birds are enormously varied. There are about 8,500 living species, divided into 27 orders. They are all quite similar to one another in basic structure, but differ in proportions and living habits. All birds have feathers and wings, even those that do not fly. No modern bird has teeth; the sharp beak serves for cutting or crushing in their stead.

There are birds in every area of the world; even the frigid Antarctic can boast of penguins. In fact, because of their fantastic migrations, the same species can be seen in Canada at one season and in South America at another.

Generally speaking, those birds that cannot fly are larger and have much stronger legs than those that do fly. In running birds, like ostriches, rheas, and cassowaries, the wings are very much reduced in size. Their bones are heavier, having no air cavities as do those of flying birds. Although they do not fly, ostriches and rheas are fast runners with feet that are long and strong.

Penguins, too, are flightless birds. Rather than running speed, they depend upon swimming ability. Underwater, they are able to swim as fast as seals.

Kiwis, too, are flightless. But they differ from other flightless birds in several respects. They have nostrils near the tip of the bill, providing them with a well-developed sense of smell. This is very rare for birds, who, like man, rely much more heavily on sight. There is no external trace of wings. Nor are there tail feathers of any kind. Actually, the entire body is covered with feathers that look more like hair. Kiwis live in dense forests. If they are in a hurry they can outrun a dog.

In contrast to flightless birds, albatrosses of the cold southerly reaches of the earth are almost unbelievable masters of the skies. Some albatrosses make a complete round-the-world tour between breeding seasons.

Second to flight, the ability most admired in birds is song. The range of sounds used for communication in these animals is exceptional. Some common birds, however, are mute. This is true of the stork, who compensates by way of an elaborate series of postures and a wild clacking of the beak.

Some swans are also mute. In general, though, most birds in its family, the Ana-tidae, have loud, raucous voices. The family includes ducks, geese, and swans. All these waterfowl have short legs and a short, broad bill. In addition to being great swimmers, most of them are excellent fliers.

Birds of prey are also marvelous fliers. They are divided into two orders. Those that fly by day, the eagles, hawks, and vultures, belong to the order Falconiformes. They are beautifully-adapted predators, with long wings for sustained flight and feet ending in sharp talons, for tearing apart flesh. Their eyesight is keener than that of most vertebrates, for there are two focusing points in each eye, one for close objects and another for distant objects. The powerful beak is sharply hooked. The entire body, even in the smallest hawks, gives the impression of great power.

The night-hunting birds of prey are the owls. They belong to the order Strigiformes. They are different from the Falconiformes in their very soft, downy feathers which reach to the toes, and the out-sized head with its small beak and huge, frontally set eyes. Owls can make some terrifying sounds when at leisure. However, while they are at work hunting they are absolutely silent, an ability enhanced by their soft plumage.

During breeding time, boobies (opposite page) like to flock together in groups. They stay on rocky islands near the schools of fish they prey upon.

The hornbill (below left) has breeding habits as strange as its appearance. After mating, the female is walled into a hollow in a tree for the duration of the incubation period. She must be fed by the male during this time.

The toucan (below right) has an enormous bill. This bill is honeycombed with air chambers; thus it does not weigh much. It does not hinder the toucan's flight and is a fine tool for tearing fruits and berries off branches.

The peacock (center) belongs to the same order as chickens, turkeys, and pheasants. Canadian geese (bottom) belong in an order with swans and ducks.

The European spoonbill (right) is closely related to the ibises and like them is very sociable. Spoonbills breed in marshes in nests about one foot above the mud. They use their large bills to sweep over the water and filter out the small invertebrates they feed upon.

The California quail (below) lives in grasslands and semiarid areas. Although quail can fly, they spend much of their time on the ground. They often run rather than fly when alarmed.

Of all the birds, those of the order Galliformes have been most important to mankind. This order includes our domestic fowl as well as our favorite game birds. Chickens, turkeys, pheasants, partridges, grouse, and quail all belong in this order. Characteristic of every one is a small head on a thick-set body. The legs are long, and the strong feet are built for scratching the earth in search of seeds. Most species have short wings, precluding the possibility of long migratory flights. Most of these species boast males of exquisite plumage, high combs, wattles, and spurs. A striking example is the peacock.

The constant drumming sounds made by woodpeckers as they drill their way through to food is enough to attract anyone's attention. Once noticed, they continue to captivate with their straight-tailed vertical hopping up and down insect-laden trees. They belong to the order Piciformes.

Over half the species of living birds belong to a single order—the Passeriformes. These include all our songbirds, such as the robins, wrens, sparrows, and thrushes. In addition to the beauty added to our lives by the lilting song of these small birds, there is an economic reason for their popularity. Songbirds are indispensable agents in ridding the world of agricultural pests such as locusts and caterpillars.

Passerines occur in all the major land areas of the world except Antarctica. They dominate the air. Their feet are distinctive. Each foot has four toes joined at the same level, three in front and one behind. The hind toe is the strongest. The purpose of such a foot is to grasp firmly to a small perch while offering full support to the bird. This foot is also useful in hopping or walking. We are more likely, however, to be aware of the highly developed voice box, which is the other outstanding feature of these birds.

The scarlet macaw (left) is a member of the parrot family. Parrots fly straight and very rapidly.

The golden eagle (below), like all eagles, uses all forms of flight in hunting. Eagles are especially expert in soaring.

The booby (lower left) flies with head, neck, and body in a straight line. It extends its wings out to the sides like airplane wings.

Mammals

Long ago, in the very beginning of reptile evolution, before the advent of dinosaurs, one line of reptiles took a completely different path from the others. They developed into animals with teeth designed for cutting and chewing rather than for grabbing and swallowing whole. The vertebral column was very strong. The legs, which lifted the body high off the ground, had knees pointing forward and elbows pointing backward. These reptiles were, in fact, almost mammalian and are referred to as mammal-like reptiles.

From the mammal-like reptiles it was a short step to the complete mammal—an ani-

Mammals, like this group of lions, are the dominant life form today. There are 18 orders of living mammals in the world. Lions belong to the order Carnivora. Most mammals of this order are hunters and eaters of meat.

mal distinguished by its constant high body temperature, its covering of hair and fur, and its production of milk for the young.

The first mammals were rather innocuous animals: small, scurrying creatures that existed on insects. Inasmuch as they were inhabiting what was then the dinosaur's world, it was probably just as well that they were inconspicuous. For millions of years, while the reptiles predominated, mammals remained modest forest creatures. Then, when the dinosaurs became extinct, the mammals, with new niches open, began to expand in both numbers and varieties. Suddenly, the world became a mammal-dominated place and has remained so to this day.

Lions live in groups called prides. A pride includes lions of both sexes and all ages. Although lions once roamed from Africa to India, they have been greatly restricted by mankind. They now live mainly in protected areas of Africa and in the Gir forest in India.

Mammals are a highly diversified class. Here are six representatives of different mammal groups: an Old World mouse of the order Rodentia (top, left); an Australian wombat of the Marsupialia (bottom, left); a three-toed sloth of the Edentata (top, right); an orangutan of the Primates (opposite page, left); a rabbit of the Lagomorpha (opposite page, upper right); and an aardvark of the order Tubulidentata (opposite page, below).

From almost the earliest part of mammalian history, there have been two distinct groups: the marsupial mammals and the placental mammals. Most living mammals belong to the placental group. The name denotes the presence of an internal structure known as a placenta, by way of which the young are nourished while within the mother's body. Marsupials have slightly-developed young that attach to the mother's nipples for future development.

Marsupials are less successful than placental mammals in that there are now fewer of them. They are now restricted in range to Australia and parts of North and South America. In addition to their less advanced method of reproduction, marsupials have the disadvantage of an inferior intelligence.

In North and South America, there are few living marsupials. However, at one time in their history, they were more diverse. The most flourishing marsupial has been the opossum, which has spread out in recent years to increase its range northward.

Australia, which has remained isolated throughout most of history, has been the real haven of the marsupials. Until the coming of man, they had the whole continent mainly to themselves with little placental competition (except for some specialized rats, and bats). Here we find an extraordinary range of marsupials: plains-dwelling grazers like the kangaroos, shy arboreal creatures such as koalas, and fierce predators like Tasmanian "wolves" and "devils."

Another group of mammals also exists in Australia and New Guinea. These primitive animals are the monotremes. They are egg-

laying mammals, more closely related to their reptile ancestors than are either the marsupials or placentals. In several respects, the skeleton is quite similar to that of the reptiles. Although monotremes are warm-blooded, their temperatures fluctuate more than those of other mammals. The platypus and the echidna form the two families in this order.

The other 16 orders of mammals are all placentals. These animals, beginning with small insectivore forebears, have spread out and diversified in so many shapes and sizes that their success is obvious. Adaptations of every sort have been made, so that there are mammals that fly, and mammals that swim, mammals that climb trees and mammals that dig burrows, as well as those that live on land. There are plant-eaters, meat-eaters, insect-eaters, and carrion-eaters. Big and small, mammals are the rulers.

The most ancient order of placental mammals and in many ways the most primitive, is that of the Insectivora. Insectivores are small and inconspicuous. Most of them have long snouts, small sharp teeth, and five clawed toes on each foot. Insectivores include shrews, moles, and hedgehogs.

Bats and flying lemurs, because of their special aerial adaptations, are placed in separate orders—the Chiroptera and the Dermoptera, respectively. They are, however, quite similar to the insectivores in many aspects. Bats are second only to the rodents in number of species—there are about 875 species. These bats have varied habits and diets. Flying lemurs are not lemurs. Nor do they actually fly. They are built for gliding, and the common name colugo is probably less confusing.

Sloths, anteaters, and armadillos are all members of the order Edentata (meaning without teeth). However, sloths and armadillos do have teeth. There are 31 species in this order, all of which live in South America, Central America, or the southern part of North America.

At one time, rabbits, hares, and pikas were classified as rodents. Now they are separated into another order, the Lagomorpha. They occupied a great portion of the land areas of the world before the coming of man. Since then they have been introduced, with overwhelming success, into regions they had not previously occupied.

Pangolins are unique animals. Their bodies are covered with overlapping, sharp-edged scales that are movable. The eight species constitute their own order, the Pholidota. They live only in the tropics of Africa and Asia.

Rodents are the most flourishing of all mammals in terms of numbers and adaptability. There are 1,600 species in the order Rodentia. Included among them are rats,

Rhinoceroses are members of the order Perissodactyla. Horses and tapirs are other important members of this order. Rhinoceroses live in parts of Asia and Africa. Pictured here are African black rhinoceroses, the most common species. Black rhinos are short-tempered and unpredictable. They have been known to throw men into the air with their front horn.

Antelopes (left) belong to an order of hoofed mammals, the Artiodactyla. This order has been far more successful than the perissodactyls. Mankind's most important meat animals belong to this group—pigs, sheep, goats, and cattle. The order also includes deer and giraffes.

The gorilla (below) belongs to the order Primates. It is the largest of the manlike apes. The average height of a gorilla is about five feet with the knees bent. The chest measures about 70 inches around.

mice, squirrels, gophers, guinea pigs, hamsters, porcupines, gerbils, beavers, and muskrats, to name but a few. All rodents have four constantly growing incisors, two on the upper jaw and two on the lower jaw.

The Cetacea includes the largest animals of all times, the whales. It also includes the porpoises. There are 84 species of cetaceans living in the oceans of the world. They have adapted completely to the sea and never return to land.

This black panther (left) is really a solid-black leopard. Note its large teeth, which function as weapons in hunting.

137

The great hunting mammals belong to the order Carnivora. Wolves, lions, weasels, mongooses, and hyenas are all carnivores, as are domestic dogs and cats. But non-hunting animals such as the pandas are also members of this group, as are the ominvorous bears and racoons. Most carnivores are running or climbing animals, but the otters are aquatic. All species have clawed feet, well-developed brains, and one pair of cheek teeth specially developed for shearing. These teeth are called carnassials.

Seals, sea lions, and walruses are also in the Carnivora, although they have sometimes been split into their own order, Pinnipedia. They live along the coasts of the world; most species live in temperate or polar waters.

Pinnipeds have torpedo-shaped bodies with all four legs transformed into flippers.

The aardvarks are placed in the Order Tubulidentata. They live in Africa south of the Sahara, wherever large colonies of ants and termites are to be found.

Two species of elephants are the only remaining members of the Proboscidea; not too long ago there were many more kinds of these massive animals roaming throughout every continent except Australia. Aside from its great size, an elephant's most conspicuous characteristic is its trunk, a long, flexible extension of the nose and upper lip.

Oddly enough, the two orders most closely related to the Proboscidea are the Hyracoidea and the Sirenia. The first of these includes

Sea lions are pinnipeds, in the order Carnivora. Unlike seals, who must wriggle on their bellies on land, sea lions can use all four limbs for walking.

the little hyraxes of biblical fame. Hyraxes look like rodents, but they have distinctive teeth and flat, hoof-like nails.

The Sirenia are the dugongs and manatees. They are sometimes referred to as sea cows. They live along tropical coasts, grazing on water vegetation. They have fore legs that are paddle-shaped, but no hind legs.

Perissodactyls are hoofed plant-eaters with an odd number of toes. At one time, there were many families, but now there are only three: horses, tapirs, and rhinoceroses. They are all well-adapted to running, their common characteristic being that the weight-bearing axis of the foot passes through the middle toe. That toe, then, is either the biggest or the sole remaining one in the foot.

Even-toed plant-eaters, classified as the Artiodactyla, have been much more successful. There are nine living families, which include several of our most important food animals. Pigs, hippopotamuses, camels, deer, giraffes, antelopes, sheep, goats, and cattle all belong in this order. Artiodactyls bear their weight between the third and fourth toe. They always retain at least these two toes, making most of them cloven-hoofed.

Primates are of great interest to mankind, for it is the order to which we belong. There are several families in the order: lemurs, tarsiers, monkeys, and apes are some of them. Most primates live in tropical areas. Common to the order are forwardly-directed eyes, grasping hands, and a well-developed brain.

Mammals have adapted to every type of environment. The hippo (left) is a river-dwelling animal of Africa. The tapir (below) lives in wooded areas of Mexico and Central and South America. Dolphins (bottom center) are completely water-dwelling mammals; they are found in all the oceans of the world.

"Missing Links" Between Vertebrates and Invertebrates

This is a colony of small, saclike animals called sea squirts, or tunicates. They are chordates, as are all the vertebrates. These primitive animals consist mainly of a feeding apparatus—a basketlike structure. Water passes through the structure, while food particles are trapped inside.

It is rather easy for us to see that vertebrates are related to one another. It does not strain our imagination to conceive of fishes, amphibians, reptiles, birds, and mammals as sharing many common denominators of ancestry and relationship. But what is the relationship between vertebrates and invertebrates? What are the missing links between these two types of animals?

Scientists place the vertebrates in a major grouping, or phylum, called the Chordata. In the same phylum are several relatively insignificant kinds of marine animals: tongue worms, tunicates, and lancelets. The common characteristic uniting all these organisms is the possession of an internal stiffening rod called a notochord. In vertebrates, notochords are present during their embryonic development; usually it is later replaced by bony or cartilaginous discs. In the other chordates, the notochord remains an unsegmented rod or disappears entirely in the adult.

A very representative chordate, and one that shows all of the general morphology of a chordate, is the lancelet amphioxus. Amphioxus lives in shallow, sandy-bottomed habitats in all the oceans. It is only about two inches long. It is basically fishlike in shape, with structures that can be seen to lead quite naturally to those of jawless fishes. The head region is not set off from the rest of the body and has no separate eyes, nose, ears, or jaws.

The front third of Amphioxus, however, behind the mouth, is provided with several hundred gill slits, piercing the pharynx and covered by folds of the body wall. Feeding and respiration take place by means of currents set up by thousands of tiny hairs on the cells that line the gill bars between the slits. Water containing food and oxygen is drawn in through the mouth into the pharynx and expelled through the slits. The food particles get stuck to a slimy mucus that is secreted by the cells along the bottom of the pharynx. The food is then moved further along to the intestine.

Although there are many differences between amphioxus and a vertebrate such as a fish, the similarities are overwhelming. There is the all-important notochord. Above this lies a hollow central nerve cord; below it is the digestive tube. There are the gill bars; these lie between the gill slits and contain blood vessels. Also, both organisms have a musculature that is segmented into bundles of muscle fibers called myotomes. All in all, although no good fossil evidence exists, we can conclude that the first vertebrates must have passed through an amphioxus-like stage.

Another group of invertebrate chordates, unlike amphioxus, seem very far-fetched indeed as relatives to fish and man. These are the sea squirts, or tunicates. Most of these animals are small, saclike creatures. They live attached to the sea floor and obtain their food by filter-feeding. The body consists mainly of a huge pharynx, slitted with openings that are lined with ciliated cells. Here we see the similarity to the feeding apparatus described for amphioxus.

However, to find more apparent chordate characteristics, we must look at the larval

The photograph on the bottom shows clearly the segmented muscles of amphioxus. The structure of the throat area, with its hundreds of gill openings, can be seen from the drawing above the photo. Observe the notochord and overlying nerve cord along the back. This kind of arrangement is also typical for the vertebrates.

The free-moving larvae of certain tunicates look like tadpoles (far left). The head region contains sense organs and a feeding device.

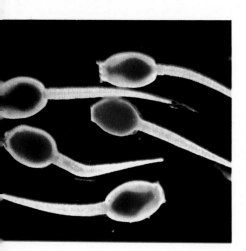

tunicates. The larvae, unlike their parents, are not attached but free-swimming. They have a tadpolelike appearance, with a head and a tail region through which runs the notochord. Above the notochord is a hollow central nerve canal.

An interesting, though unproven, theory is that some hundreds of millions of years ago, certain ancient tunicate larve, instead of developing into sessile (attached) adults, by-passed this stage by the process of paedomorphosis. This process can be observed among species of animals today. It consists of the attainment of sexual maturity during the larval stage. Thus the adults actually look like the larvae of their ancestors. Some scientists think that certain tunicate larvae, through paedomorphosis, evolved into amphioxus-like forms which were at the base of all vertebrate evolution.

Now let's consider the invertebrates. These include worms, snails, crabs, jellyfish, and starfish. Where among these many varied body plans should we look for chordate relatives?

Surprisingly, it is the echinoderms—the group to which the starfish, sea urchins, sea cucumbers, and sea lilies belong—that are the closest invertebrate relatives to the chordates. The echinoderms are the only invertebrates that have one essential characteristic in common with the chordates: the manner in which the fertilized eggs first develop. There are also features of the nervous system, the development of muscle fibers and hard parts, and certain very specific biochemical similarities that all point toward echinoderms as the closest invertebrate link to primitive chordates and vertebrates.

The larvae of echinoderms also provide a clue to possible relationships. Unlike echinoderm adults, which are radically symmetrical, the larvae are bilaterally symmetrical; that is, the two halves of the body form mirror images of one another. Chordates—including tunicate larvae, amphioxus, turtles, birds, and human beings—are also bilateral.

Some zoologists hypothesize that ancient echinoderms and chordates shared a common, and as yet completely unknown, ancestor. This ancestor had echinodermlike larvae that evolved into the kind of larvae now possessed by tunicates. Then through paedomorphosis, the then-typical attached adult stage was by-passed. Evolutionary emphasis centered around the larval characteristic of free motion through water. The fish shape and the segmented musculature around a supporting notochord were the results of this selection.

We can summarize these main evolutionary steps between invertebrates and vertebrates as follows: An echinoderm-like animal gave rise to a tunicate-like chordate whose larvae reproduced while still in the free-swimming stage. These, in turn, passed through an amphioxus-like stage. Finally, the first vertebrates, the jawless fishes, evolved.

In the following volumes we will take a closer look at the evolution of vertebrates. Although fossils provide much evidence to support our evolutionary theories, there are still unknown "missing links".

Shown below is the larva of a starfish. It has two mirror-image body halves. This makes it similar in body plan to the tunicate larva. Most zoologists think that echinoderms, tunicates, amphioxus, and the vertebrates are evolutionary branchings from the same line of descent.

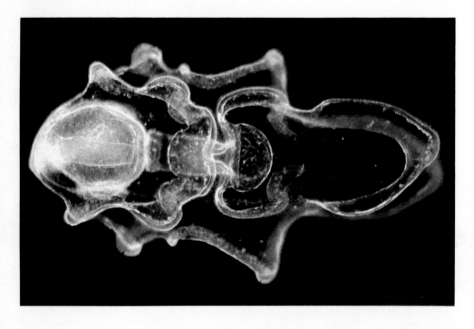

Index Italicized page numbers refer to illustrations.